the

girls
guide

to getting
it on

FLIC EVERETT

the girls' guide to getting it on

What every girl should know about sex

Thorsons

Thorsons
An Imprint of HarperCollins*Publishers*
77–85 Fulham Palace Road
Hammersmith, London W6 JB

The Thorsons website address is:
www.thorsons.com

and *Thorsons*
are trademarks of
HarperCollins*Publishers* Limited

Published by Thorsons 2001

1 3 5 7 9 10 8 6 4 2

© Flic Everett 2001

Flic Everett asserts the moral right to be
identified as the author of this work

A catalogue record for this book is
available from the British Library

ISBN 0 00 712414 7

Printed and bound in Great Britain by
Omnia Books Ltd, Glasgow

Contents

Introduction

If sex is such a natural phenomenon, how come there are so many books on how to do it?

Bette Midler

Oh, not another sex book ... haven't you had enough of these endless manuals that tell you exactly where you're going wrong, which bits you should be twiddling, and how to have a multiple orgasm with only a feather duster and a tube of KY jelly? I have. Which is why this particular sex book is a little more realistic about the whole thing. We haven't got any 'real-life couples' revealing their bedroom secrets – everyone naturally suspects they're made up. And we haven't got any po-faced Sex Therapist 'Arousal Graphs', or dismal sections on the biological ins and outs. We haven't *even* got any doctors. So you're just going to have to make do with me, your self-appointed 'sexpert', with years of experience at my disposal.

I'm not assuming here that you've been married for years, or that you're with a long-term partner, or even that you've got a boyfriend at all. In fact, I'm simply assuming that you have a man you like enough to have sex with – and, if not, one who occasionally puts in an appearance – and that sometimes you could do with just a little help in making it all run smoothly.

Sex is not like it is in the movies (if it was, we'd all be doing it 15 times an hour to get it right, with microphones suspended above our heads). It's frequently embarrassing, awkward, funny, confusing, or simply dull. But sometimes it's fantastic, which is what makes us keep on doing it.

And like any important subject, the more you know, the better it gets. Which is why I've generously done all the hard work for you – and all you need to do to get it on with absolute confidence should be in this book. Unless, of course, the guy you've picked is utterly useless in bed. And even I can't help you there, I'm afraid.

CHAPTER ONE

When and where to have sex

Love is the answer, but while you're waiting for the answer, sex raises some pretty good questions.

Woody Allen

Let's assume you already know a man you find reasonably attractive – the idea of removing his trousers isn't instantly repellent, and when musing on his penis, you don't automatically think 'Aargh ... purple and angry!' but 'Mm ... smooth and appealing'. But unless you happen to be living amongst a primitive Amazonian tribe, for whom the idea of leaping on any passing male and taking him then and there on the forest floor is entirely normal, there are certain issues you need to deal with first. Like when to have sex. And when you've worked that out, where to have it.

The obvious answer to 'When have sex?' would be 'Whenever anyone asks nicely enough.' But as we all know, nothing's ever that simple, is it? Because although we are, naturally, women of the world, who are perfectly capable of catching a strange man's eye and winking suggestively – at least, we are after five brandy-and-Cokes –

deciding when to actually get naked with him is fraught with difficulty.

sex on first meeting – possibly unwise

Let's say you've already met a nice bloke, you've exchanged chit-chat about what you do, what your cat's called, why 'Fluffy' is, in fact, an original and vibrant choice. Then he's done that flirt-thing that all men do, of 'casually' brushing the hair out of your eyes, or 'idly' examining your pendant – incidentally, don't ever think that a man is actually interested in jewellery craftsmanship when he playfully examines your necklace/bracelet/earring/nipple piercing. Unless he's a Swiss watch-maker, it's a pathetically obvious attempt to brush against your skin.

So you'll probably end the evening with some form of bodily contact. He, generally, would like that bodily contact to be the kind of sex that oil-rig workers fantasize about when gazing at a life-size poster of Jennifer Lopez. Whether you know each other's names or not is largely irrelevant, so long as you can manage to say 'Yes!' or 'More!' or 'Oh God, you're so huge I don't know if I … yes! It fits!' Then, when you're tangled sweatily in each other's post-coital embrace, he can decide whether he likes you enough to see you again, or whether he should make his excuses and leave before you develop an unwieldy affection for him.

I know, it's unpleasant. But most single young men out for a night on the beer do not approach the pub thinking, 'I wonder if I'll meet the woman of my dreams tonight and get to know her gradually over a period of months?' They think 'Will I pull?'

Now, if you want instant gratification, the just-add-water-and-stir of sex, there's nothing wrong with a wild, hedonistic shagging spree that will end next morning with mutual pleas-antries before he disappears forever. But if you've met the nice man, had the cat-conversation, laughed together at the feeble pulling-antics of his mates, and he didn't examine your pendant too cheesily, you may well want a little more than a one-night carnival. So your version of bodily contact at the end of the evening may be simply a chaste kiss, and an exchange of phone numbers.

Of course, if you like him, and he's also driving you berserk with lust just by breathing, there's no rule that says if you have sex the first night he'll disappear out of your life next day. He may get up, make you breakfast and stay for a week, intermittently crooning love songs and plaiting rosebuds into your hair. Then again, there's no rule that says if you eat 15 meat and potato pies at one sitting, you'll feel bad either – but, somehow, you just know it's not a great idea.

When debating whether to have sex the night you meet, ask yourself, 'Do I care if I have sex and never see this person again?' And then ask yourself, 'Do I care if I have sex and then can't get rid of this person?' If the answer to either question is 'Yes', then don't do it.

first date sex

Let's suppose you've had your taxi-rank snog, and he rang you to arrange a further meeting after a respectable amount of time (current thinking suggests up to two and a half days; any longer, he's either forgetful, playing it way too cool, or else waiting for a chance to get away from his wife and two adorable toddlers to call you). It's the First Date. So if it goes well, and he doesn't say anything controversial, like, 'Actually, I really don't think women should work', the question is, do you have sex afterwards? Again, only you know how many pulsing currents of lust are crackling between you – the only thing is, if you aren't the sort of girl who happily puts it about, and you prefer to form some sort of meaningful relationship before you get naked, it's a little soon. My personal research suggests that it takes at least three months to really know someone – till then, everyone's on their best behaviour, tiptoeing round feelings, offering the dating equivalent of cucumber sandwiches and Earl Grey tea. People are only emboldened to reveal their true colours when they feel safe – and it's unusual to feel like the best of old buddies when all you've done together is sit through a Tom Cruise movie and share a bag of tortilla chips.

If this person is the love of your life, it won't hurt to wait a little longer, because you're going to have to stagger through another 70 years side by side, and it'd be a shame for your first sexual experience to be memorable only because it was a fumbling disaster, due to nerves. If not, and you think it could be a fun fling, then feel free to shag away. It's obvious that the best sex usually happens when you know someone pretty well – but sex when you hardly know someone at all but fancy the pants off them can also be good. Bearing in mind, of course, that the grannies who pursed their lips and muttered that men are only after one thing were not always right – but sometimes they were. And while, hey, any liberated woman can decide for herself when she wants to sleep with her man, she also shouldn't be surprised if the said man doesn't bother to return calls after first date sex.

A friend of mine used to call first date sex 'the creme egg theory' – it looks gorgeous, you think you want it, you gobble it up really fast – then it's just horribly sickly, you feel crap about yourself, and frankly, you wish you hadn't bothered. Basically, first date sex – fine if you want to, but often there won't be much substance to it. If you think it could be a good relationship, you'll probably have more fun if you wait a while.

sex a few dates later – very sensible, dear

What about a few dates into your blossoming relationship? Indeed, this is prime 'having sex' territory. You can get to the stage of being able to see past the heaving bosoms and bulging trousers to check that one of you isn't a) a fascist, b) psychotic or c) fundamentally sad and desperate – though this is by no means foolproof – but you're not at the stage of discussing commitment, getting jealous about exes, or nagging. This is a delicate time in any relationship, and it doesn't last long, so having sex now can store up goodwill for the future. Which you'll probably need, to be honest. The classic getting-to-bed routine involves a couple of dates of serious fondling (which forbidding signs in my local swimming baths used to call 'petting', though why anyone would want to 'pet' in a malodorous public pool watched by shrieking eight-year-olds is beyond me). He'll approach your best knickers – because you aren't remotely at the stage of going back to comfy ones yet, and are probably still pretending you wear stockings and suspenders for the sheer fun of it – and you'll say, 'Oh, that's nice', and then he'll try to get most of your clothes off, with you tugging them back on coquettishly, like a Victorian lady in a seaside bathing hut. At some point, he'll attempt to get both his and your genitals naked at the same time, and you'll say 'Oh, er, it's a bit soon ...' and, being well-brought up, he'll do his trousers up and smile politely.

A couple of dates after this teen-style fumbling happens, you will have the Seduction Date, which probably involves someone cooking a meal for someone else, candlelight, and a drunken glow which results in a fantastic shag. And then, after you've done it once, you can do it again any old time you want.

So, a few dates in – let's say four or five – is standard practice for when to have sex successfully. Like anything to do with sex, it's never foolproof – but it's enough time to know a bit about him. And it's not long enough to have turned sex into a vast, insurmountable obstacle.

sex as a vast, insurmountable obstacle

Of course, you may be deeply religious. In which case, you really shouldn't be reading a book like this, because it will only upset you, and you'll probably end up having to burn it anyway. If you are defying your elders to flick through it, you may also think that sex before marriage is a very bad idea, leading to unclean thoughts, disease, and so on. Well, we're dealing with disease later, and most unclean thoughts are probably covered in between. So you stay celibate, have fun, and come back and show us the 90-foot tapestry you ploughed your womanly urges into in a few years' time.

As for the rest of you ... Of course you want to get to know this man well before you commit your body to him. Some women like to hear him say, 'I love you' first. Hence the number of sexually frustrated women sitting in bed saying, 'I only want you to say it if you mean it, but do you love me?' and sexually frustrated boyfriends muttering, 'You know I'm ... fond ... deeply ... liking ... immensely ... keen ...' and wishing they weren't so bloody honest. If you want to wait till he says it of his own accord, fine – otherwise, it's a bad idea to make sex a condition of anything, unless you are going to go the whole way and make it a condition of marriage – in which case you're probably too busy raising a barn in Appalachia, or making bootees for your bottom drawer, to care what I have to say.

The trouble is, the longer you go on seeing him without having sex, the more difficult it gets to say, 'Wahey, we've been together four months, let's do it!' Sex becomes a huge, worrying step, implying all sorts of things – love, commitment, trust ... which, of course, in an ideal world it should, and if he feels the same as you do, great – but if he's used to shagging as and when the fancy takes him, he may suddenly feel he's been plunged into an Edwardian novel, and is expected to ask your father for permission before he looks at your ankles. The other worry is, if you carry on smiling kindly at each other and slapping his hand every time it travels further than your top button, sex is going to be built up into something so monumentally fantastic that anything less than heavenly choirs and soaring angels thronging the skies when you finally do it will be a bit of a let-down. So, if you have moral reasons for waiting – or, of course, if you don't feel you know him well enough – take as long as you like. But otherwise, get on with it before your bits dry up and fall off from under-use.

what if you've been friends for ages?

There is a whole area of when to have sex that's even more difficult than normal, if that's possible. Which is – what if you've known each other ages? What if you met at nursery school, and have gone through life sharing your little joys and sorrows, until one day suddenly realizing he's The One? Or, more likely, what if you met at college, shared your little rows over packets of corn-flakes and who was in the bathroom longest, and then realized later that he's The One? Or he's your friend's brother, or your work colleague, or someone else you've known for ages and have suddenly seen in a whole new light ... well, of course, should he express a mutual attraction you're welcome to jump on each other as a hungry woman would jump on a plate of jaffa cakes. But if by some horrible, evil mischance one (or both) of you should wake up and whisper, 'Oh my god, what have we done?', it pays to try an experimental snog first. Leave that to settle, and build up to sex – after all, if you've known each other since the Play-Doh table – or, even more embarrassingly, since you were a full member of the Wimmin's Rights Debating Team at college – your relationship can afford to stay semi-platonic until you're sure it's not just the eight pints and tequila chasers talking.

Just because you've known him forever, don't assume sex will come as naturally as friendship – leaping into bed with your old buddy can be a shock to the system, so it's worth taking a little time over this, because it could get serious.

✋👐When and where not to have sex

Here is your handy cut-out-and-keep guide to when and where not to do it ...

when not to have sex

1. After a friend's wedding at which you've been drinking all day. Because you'll start thinking about the glory of love, and burst into tears as you decide you're merely having

tawdry, pointless sex while your friend the bride is glorying in marital bliss three rooms along the corridor.

2. At the office party. I don't even need to explain why, but here's some key words: Mistake. Married. Boss. Unemployment. Hideous regret. See if you can arrange them into a likely morning-after scenario.

3. When you aren't feeling sexy. You'll lie in bed, undoubtedly looking gorgeous to his lustful eyes, but ruining everything by saying, 'No, not that position, my stomach hangs down' or 'God, did you hear the sound my thighs made then?' Not appealing, really.

4. When at your parents' house. Because you'll be so terrified that every creak is your dad getting up to check on you, you won't enjoy a second of it.

5. When bent on revenge – honestly, your ex does not know or care that you just picked up a smelly biker. You will not be punishing him by sleeping with this man. But you might regret it. Correction – you will regret it.

where to have sex

There's a good reason why bed is the nation's favourite place for sex. It's comfy. And if you do want to roll around passionately, you aren't going to get agonizing carpet burns, or knock over a Ming vase with your flailing limbs. Also, lying flat on your back does wonders for your stomach, even if it does make your breasts point east and west like a faulty compass, plus it's easy to go to sleep in each other's arms afterwards, without scurrying about naked, picking clothes off the sofa. But for those of us who feel that only ever doing it in bed may be just a touch middle-aged, a soupçon suburban, there are alternatives that can make you see sex in a whole new light. Even if it is the searching beam of a policeman's torch.

AROUND THE HOUSE

The kitchen

There are those who swear by sex on top of the washing machine. To my mind, it's all a bit *Confessions of A Window Cleaner* – there's something vaguely naff about balancing on a washing machine and getting off on the spin cycle. But if it works for you, who am I to knock it? It also means you aren't wasting time when you should be getting the laundry done, so it's ideal sex for houseproud girls. The kitchen, however, is a good venue – the worktops are roughly the right height to balance on with your legs around his waist, allowing for ease of thrusting, or you can pretend to be innocently washing up while he lifts your skirt and takes you from behind at the sink.

The living room

If you can't have a bed, a sofa is the next best thing. It's a simple seduction method to move from watching television cuddled up to full-on shagging, easily brought about by moving your hand onto his thigh, while he leans in to kiss your neck. The sofa provides support for a variety of positions – lean over the back so the blood rushes to your head, with him standing behind you – or he sits on it and you climb on his lap. You can do missionary, you on top, legs hooked over his shoulders – you're as free as fabric-stain protection allows. You can, of course, do it on the floor, or even, as Victoria Wood suggested, bend him over backwards on the hostess trolley. But that's not very comfortable, really.

On a table

Could be the flour-covered kitchen table, just like in *The Postman Always Rings Twice* – though does any busy woman nowadays actually know what to do with flour? Or the polished dining-room table ... or even the fold-out trestle piled with unpaid bills – just sweep them on the floor and ignore them. Having sex on a hard table-surface offers a unique sensation, as his thrusting has a lot more impact, and creates more friction than it does on the give of a soft mattress. Basically, it's like a porn movie – harder, faster, and all the rest of it. It's definitely worth trying, with you lying back on the table and him towering over you in a masterful fashion. The downsides are, your buttocks might squeak amusingly on the wooden surface as you shunt back and forth – and, unless you weigh six stone, the table legs may collapse.

In the bathroom

'Oh yes,' warble the so-called 'sexperts' ... sex in the bath is SO romantic. No it is not. It's like trying to harpoon a whale in the dark. You can't see what you're doing, you're both slipping about, the water washes away all your nice, natural lubrications and makes everything sore and scratchy, and every time you move there's a tidal wave pouring over the edge and soaking the downstairs ceiling. A shower, on the other hand, can offer a certain thrill, so long as you have those pensioner-friendly non-slip rubber mats in the bottom. It's not sexy, admittedly, but otherwise he's going to try and penetrate you passionately, you'll slip in the soap, and you'll both end up in Casualty, soaking and in pain. So, if you are going to go for it in the shower, get your balance first. And don't wear a shower cap, however much you want your hair to stay dry – at least *try* to look appealing, even if you have got mascara running down your face, and soap in your eyes.

Outside

It is entirely possible to have great sex outdoors. But you need to memorize this checklist before you even think about packing the condoms and heading off to frolic in the wide-open spaces.

1. Can anybody see you?

   Seems obvious, but just check first whether that secluded river bank is, in fact, part of an angling club, and you're about to be surprised by 15 burly men in fishing hats.

2. Can anybody hear you?

   The hedge might screen you from view, but you really don't want the nice family picnicking on the other side to overhear you gasping, 'Yes, I want your hot sausage now', or they might pop through and offer you some.

3. Will insects bite you?

   In summer, the answer is yes, yes, yes. So, unless you want spiders settling down for a little sleep in your pants, or ants wandering through your hair thinking it's Hampton Court Maze, take some insect repellent, or shag some-where more urban.

4. Will it be cold?

   In Britain? Yes, almost certainly. If you're thinking of repeating the *From Here To Eternity* moment, rolling in the surf, just remember – they were in California. You're attempting to roll passionately in sea that requires a thick coating of goose grease to swim in.

5. Will a policeman tell you off?

   Almost certainly. Unless you're on your own private land, which isn't overlooked, you could be cautioned – or, if you're getting naked in aisle 10 of Sainsbury's, arrested.

Having said that, sex outdoors can be enjoyable – a little breeze round your bits, feeling at one with nature, pretending you live somewhere hot where spontaneous acts of passion don't require a print-out of the weather forecast and a flask of cocoa. Sometimes, it's true, it can be fun. But not that often.

CHAPTER TWO

Successful seduction

Pursuit and seduction are the essence of sexuality. It's part of the sizzle.

Camille Paglia, renowned feminist

All too often nowadays, seduction consists of six pints and a quick feel in the taxi on the way home. This may be efficient, but it's hardly the way to begin a sexually charged liaison if you're hoping for more than a regrettable quickie with a man who looks like a dried-up pizza in daylight. True seduction is like a dance – and it's more of an 18th-century waltz than the podium shimmy you have in mind. There are certain moves that will lead to the required outcome a lot more successfully than grabbing his crotch in a crowded bar – if the required outcome is good sex, that is.

Of course, you may get lucky – he may seduce you. But don't count on him – most men are so terrified of misreading the signals, they'll wait until you're naked but for a feather boa, singing 'Touch me, I want your body' through a megaphone. And, even then, he might assume you mean somebody else. So, unless you've picked a particularly confident specimen, you may be required to do the initial seducing yourself. Once he's got the idea, he won't leave you alone – but just as mother cats teach their young how to wash, thus launching them on a lifetime of frantic leg-licking, you need to show your bloke a) that you want to have sex with him, and b), far more importantly, how you like to have sex.

Of course, you can seduce him over and over again, but after a while, he'll start getting used to it, and in order to achieve the same level of excitement you'll need to start wearing nurses' costumes, or calling him 'Big Dadda' or something, so ideally you'll simply concentrate on the initial seduction, and let him do most of the hard work later on.

where to seduce

Traditional seduction takes place in a conservatory full of potted palms, with him bearing down on you wearing a tail-coat, and you batting your fan about, crying 'Fie, sir! I'm simply not that sort of a gel!' However, modern seduction generally involves both participants being willing – it's simply a long build-up to the inevitable sex, taking the slow scenic route, rather than the 'Nice arse, fancy a shag?' short-cut. It's best if it happens in a secure, enclosed environment – distractions are the enemy of seduction. So if you form some plan that involves an intimate restaurant meal, followed by a candlelit winebar, you'll get halfway through the starter, and his mates will saunter past the window, spot your bloke, and invade the restaurant, brandishing invitations to a party afterwards, or a sesh back at Darren's, and before you know it you'll all be piling off to the off-licence to stock up on beers. So rule one of seduction is simple – do it at home.

what to wear

Ideally, he'll be so enamoured of you that even if you answer the door wearing an Argyll jumper, bedsocks and a pair of Lycra leggings, he'll melt and think, 'She's so cutely vulnerable ... yet so sexy.' But if he's entertaining the slightest flicker of doubt, he'll merely think, 'Why's she dressed like a Cumbrian fell-walker?' and his burgeoning desires will flicker and die. Seduction dressing is simple, but it falls into two categories.

1. YOU DON'T WANT HIM TO KNOW WHAT YOU'RE PLANNING

Say the guy in question is a friend, for whom you have yearned secretly over the years – or someone new, but you're not sure if he feels the same way. You don't want to dress like a super-vixen, for fear of reducing his erection to a tiny acorn of fright. You want to look gorgeous, but casually so. This is possible – and the most important thing is Ease of Access. Many seductions have ground to a halt, scuppered by a jumper stuck over the head, and jeans that won't pull over the boots. You will feel like a two-year-old being undressed by your mum as he mutters, 'Has this got buttons?' and tugs uselessly at your belt. So opt for simplicity – a long dress that unzips, or a top that unbuttons, with a skirt that can be undone by you, instantly, to save him vital minutes of humiliating fiddling with a Karen Millen hook-and-eye combination. Obviously, you'll be wearing your best underwear either way – never fall for the old trick of 'If I wear my baggiest grey pants, it'll stop me going too far.' It won't; you'll just remember having sex with your M&S parachute hanging off one ankle forever. And don't wear tights – they may be body-slimming, but the act of peeling extra-thick Lycra layers from your bum and hips is slightly less sexy than removing a surgical support. Not an image you want him to conjure with.

2. YOU DO WANT HIM TO KNOW WHAT YOU'RE PLANNING

Dressing for a seduction which he knows is going to happen is a different ballgame altogether. You can afford to go to town – whilst bearing in mind that there's a thin line between 'seductive' and 'lust-crazed tart'. By all means show a bit of flesh – but remember that a hint of cleavage is far sexier than an in-your-face display of heaving mammary. Men like to feel they've made the discovery themselves – they don't need a flashing neon sign saying 'Baps Here' suspended above your chest. A simple black dress, then, is ideal – it's not too over-the-top – no bloke wants to be faced with the possibility of being overpowered by Alexis Carrington (unless he's recently come out) – but it's glamorous, and incredibly sexy. A skirt that sits demurely just above your knee, but that has a little split so a wedge of thigh is visible when you sit down, is also good news. And, of course, you'll be wearing stockings. Men prefer the whole suspenders thing to hold-ups – and the other problem with hold-ups is, they leave nasty red bands round your thighs. Always wear knickers over suspenders; otherwise, his hand – or, even worse, his willy – will be trapped as he tries to explore. And, of course, wear high heels, and leave these and your stockings on throughout.

your seduction environment

The best seduction environment is warm, with gentle lighting that hides flaws, sumptuous rugs and cushions, and absolute privacy. Basically, a suite at the Ritz or a snow-covered log cabin in the Rockies. Anything else is merely compromise. But assuming that, for the moment, you're stuck with your house/flat/bedroom, there are ways of changing it from the lived-in, friendly, utterly normal bolthole it is now, to a Seduction Nest made for two – it'll be more cobbled together than the Palace of Versailles made over by *Changing Rooms*, but with the right music and lighting that won't matter. It's only got to look good temporarily. The most important thing to do in the living room – and, of course, bedroom – is tidy up. If he's distracted by a pile of old newspapers, a takeaway carton and six empty wine bottles, he won't be able to concentrate for wondering whether you're a lonely alcoholic – and, if not, who you've been drinking with? Gather up all the cushions you can find, and scatter them on the sofa. Draw the curtains, turn the heat up a notch – the fewer clothes the better, and no one gets turned on when they're shivering – plus it gives you the chance to murmur, 'Is it hot in here or is it just me?' in the best tradition of porn movies. Anything overly girly – stuffed animals, posters of naked men, naff cards with life-affirming messages, and books about feng shui – hide them. There's plenty of time later in your relationship for him to discover the horrible truth.

If you have any drapey material, now's the time to get it out, and transform the sofa into something suitably sultan's – tent-like – or pin it above the bed, so it fans down around the pillows. And, of course, lighting is essential. An overhead light will instantly make your carefully styled room look like a suburban dentist's waiting room. And, however seductive that suburban dentist is, he isn't going to help your cause. Turn it off and, instead, place a lamp or two, with 40-watt bulbs, in discreet corners of the room. Contrary to popular sexpert (so-called) opinion, I don't recommend lighting the place with loads of candles, for three reasons:

1. They're a fire risk, and the smoke alarm having hysterics while you're trying to kiss your way up his left thigh won't improve things one bit.
2. They don't give much light out – hence, medieval peasants went to bed at dusk, because in candlelight they could barely see each other's potato-like heads. And it helps if he doesn't trip over five times on the way to bed.
3. They scream 'desperation' louder than a 45-year-old virgin in a miniskirt. He will think, 'Jesus, I'm being seduced!', which is all very well, but it's nicer if it appears to be mutual desire, rather than a carefully orchestrated plan of yours. Plus, you really don't want to come across like the mad person with the candlelit shrine in detective dramas, because they always end up dead by the end credits. OK?

A WORD ABOUT MUSIC

Music is a vital part of the seduction experience – for one thing, it neatly covers all the embarrassing noises that sound like nesting hamsters made by two people trying to get each other's clothes off. And, for another, it sets a mood. Avoid the temptation to play something classical, unless you're the type of girl who listens to Schubert in your spare time for fun. And Ravel's *Bolero* is a bit full-on. Also, totally avoid any music that appears to be describing your situation – particularly if it's the Beatles singing 'Eleanor Rigby' – you really don't want them warbling, 'Aah, look at all the lonely people ...' as you attempt to make conversation. Offputting feminist anthems are also out. 'No Scrubs' may be a great song, but he doesn't want to be presented with an agenda the moment he walks in. Instead, go for slow, ambient dance music – it does not mean anything embarrassing, but it's got the right beat for a seduction – Massive Attack's *Blue Lines* is the best seduction album I've ever heard and, failing that, you won't go wrong with a bit of Miles Davis-type jazz. If you were thinking of alternating Celine Dion and Whitney Houston, just one word: No.

what to do

So you've got your draped sofa, your outfit, the music – but what's he going to do, come round and be instantly jumped? Not if you've a classy bone in your body, madam. The obvious, can't-fail seduction technique is, of course, to cook him a meal. And if your cookery never progressed past 'Tuna Surprise' in third-year Home Economics, then provide (i.e. buy) a meal instead. Here, though, are the meals not to provide:

1. Spaghetti bolognese – no one looks attractive sucking strands from a plate. With the exception of the dogs in *Lady and the Tramp*.
2. Pizza – cheese strands linking your mouth to the plate. Greasy fingers. Bits of pepperoni on your best dress. It's not attractive, is it?
3. Anything involving industrial quantities of garlic, onions or mustard – bad breath and wind aren't your best companions on a hot date.
4. Bony fish – bundling a choking man into an ambulance is not how you want the date to end.

5. A four-course meal. He won't be able to move, let alone have rampant sex.

And here are the meals you can provide with confidence – with recipes:

1. A selection of pre-bought appealing nibbles – we're talking relatively sophisticated stuffed vine leaves, taramasalata, and salsa dip, though – not jam tarts and pickled onion crisps.
2. Fillet steak in red wine sauce, with baby vegetables and potatoes – Ask how he likes steak cooked first, then sear it in the pan before cooking it through in the sauce – which you can make with mushrooms, tinned tomatoes, red wine, and herbs. Steam the vegetables lightly – and, rather than chips, parboil the potatoes, then chop them into cubes, put them in an ovenproof dish with garlic, mixed herbs, salt and pepper and a coating of olive oil. Cook on medium heat in the oven till crispy, turning occasionally.
3. Chicken in a creamy sauce with rice – Grill the chicken, make the sauce with mushrooms, chicken stock, crème fraîche and white wine, and before serving the rice, pack it into a teacup and then turn it onto the plate for a dazzling rice-tower effect. People pay good money for this in restaurants.
4. Salmon with new potatoes – Bake the salmon with a squeeze of lemon juice and pepper, wrapped in foil. Boil new potatoes, dab them with butter, and serve with garden peas (as opposed to Jungle Peas – what other kind of peas are there?) or mangetout.
5. Kitten pie – Just kidding: I need to check you're paying attention occasionally.

The most important thing to remember about all this is judge the amount correctly. A lot of men can't function when they're starving. So even if you're going for your usual hip-and-thigh-diet gnat-feeding portions, at least provide lots of French bread, cheese, tortilla chips and so on, within easy reach. On the other hand, don't overfeed him, because he'll be pinned to his chair like Father Christmas after a reindeer-stew blow-out.

And drink – wine is more likely to put him in the right frame of mind than beer. But don't knock it back in your nervousness – you comatose and him with brewer's droop really isn't an ideal outcome.

making your move

Look, it's really not that hard to seduce a man. The slightest encouraging touch from you, and most men will be poised over their buttons, ready to shed all. But if you want to do it right, and get yourself in the mood too, you need to start before you actually touch him. You can do a lot with body language – semaphore, for instance. But you probably won't need that skill on this occasion. Just restrict your flirtatious gestures to brushing his arm, picking imaginary fluff off his shoulder, and the occasional knee-tap to make a point. You can also make prolonged eye contact, with the hint of a smile playing about your lips. Though, if he's telling you about how his mum's operation went wrong, you may want to back-pedal on the smile. Laugh at his jokes, but don't cackle like a pissed 14-year-old whenever he says anything mildly witty. And, of course, you're free to laugh at any jokes you might make – they're probably wittier than his, so get your laughs while you can, as it's all going to get serious in a minute.

After dinner, you will suggest you go and sit on the couch with your coffee, or your large brandies, tumblers of absinthe – whatever. And then you'll steer the chat around to sex. Not by saying, 'Bloody hell, do I have to do everything myself?' and ripping your dress off – but by inserting enough innuendo into the conversation to get him hotter than a chilli in a sauna. It's easy if you know how – but here are some sample 'sex-steering' comments for you to use ...

'It's nice to have you here – and you can take that any way you choose…'

Talk generally about your adolescence – and add, 'So, when did you lose your virginity?'

Tell him you like his shirt, and say, 'Can I just feel the fabric? It's silk, isn't it?'

Offer to read his palm, and tell him he's got a highly developed sex drive, according to his mount of Venus.

Ask him if he's a cat or dog person – if he says cat, sigh, 'I always think they're such sensual animals …'; if dog, breathe, 'So do you always go straight for what you want, too?'

Don't, under any circumstances, mention exes. Don't mention any illnesses you've ever had. Keep 'really close' male friends out of the equation. And don't tell him about your flatmate, who's a blonde, Swedish lapdancer.

and they're off

If none of the above leads directly to snogging, you may as well just go for it. Turn his head to face you with a light brush of finger on cheek, and gaze into his eyes. Try very hard not to look needy, although 'glazed with lust' is just about permissible. Very slowly move towards him and, if he doesn't move away, kiss him. If he does move away, you're entitled to find out why – and if he blurts, 'I'm gay', then we can only assume you've been reading the signals wrongly. If not, then you can progress to unbuttoning his shirt, and sliding your hand inside as you kiss. But don't whisk his flies open and climb on top just yet – you've spent hours preparing this little seduction scene, it'd be a shame if it was all over five minutes after the first kiss. It's time to be a little coquettish (though there's a fine line between 'coquette' and 'pricktease') – every time his hand shoots up your skirt, gently remove it and go back to kissing, rubbing and stroking his upper body. Kiss his neck, lick his ear – quietly, or it'll sound like an army marching through mud – and suck his fingers. When he's shaking with lust, and you're mere seconds from shouting,

'Come on, what are you waiting for?', allow your hand to stray to his crotch – but before you unpack him in all his glory, suggest you go into the bedroom. This is for several reasons.

Firstly, if you don't live alone, it dismisses the hideous possibility of your flatmate (particularly your blonde, lapdancer flatmate) returning from her night out to see your legs stuck in the air and a strange man's bottom doing the hokey-cokey on her sofa.

Secondly, it provides comfort, so you can concentrate on having a good time without being squashed between the coffee table and a bookcase.

Thirdly, it makes it a lot more likely that you'll remember to use contraception, because it should be right there in your bedside table.

And finally, you can go to sleep afterwards without the awful embarrassment of scuttling about collecting up strewn clothes like some nudist park-keeper.

if he seduces you

Of course, him seducing you isn't a problem – it just means he got there first. But it is a slight difficulty if he's doing it all wrong. As we all know, a seduction is a slow, gentle build-up to explosively dramatic sex. So if he starts saying things like, 'Christ, you look hot, bend over for us then,' the minute he arrives, you'll have to make it clear that he's jumping the gun. A little jokey innuendo is one thing, but suggesting that you skip the meal and go straight to bed is extremely poor form. Of course, if he's really a champion seducer you'll barely realize he's doing it – he'll simply be showering you with witty compliments, and running his fingers down your bare back, and asking you what your marvellous perfume is. Let it happen. If he isn't, though, he may lumber in with some appallingly Austin Powers-like phrases: 'You make me so horny, baby', 'Come here, I want to show you what you do to me' or even the tired old student favourite, 'Are you cold? Shall I warm you up?' ... in which case, think carefully – do you really want to seduce this man? If the answer's still yes (and there'd better be a good reason), then it's your look-out. But any man who fails to understand the basic rules of seduction is a bit of a dud in my book.

good seduction conversation topics

Are light, fun, open-ended and entertaining ...

1. What you'd do on a desert island
2. Favourite parts of your body
3. Do aliens/ghosts exist?
4. Favourite films
5. Travel
6. Sex. Obviously ...

bad seduction conversation topics

Are serious, boring, controversial, and have potential to go hideously wrong ...

1. Politics
2. Illness (particularly mental) and problems in general
3. Friends he's never met
4. Other men
5. Work

your top five seduction CDs

Anything with 'blue' in the title is a good bet:

1. *Blue Lines*, Massive Attack
2. *Kind of Blue*, Miles Davies
3. *Blue Train*, John Coltrane
4. *Betty Blue*, film score
5. Anything by Billie Holiday – it's all blues

Kissing

I wasn't kissing her, I was whispering in her mouth ...

Groucho Marx

You may recall that Jack Lemmon once said of Marilyn Monroe, his co-star in *Some Like It Hot*, that kissing her was 'like kissing Hitler'. While this was most ungentlemanly and, in fact, Marilyn probably kissed very nicely, it's worth bearing in mind that kissing is not as natural a skill as you might think. For a start, anything that involves the potential to bump noses is automatically going to be awkward. Then you've got the exchange of germs and saliva, the bad-breath fears, the clashing teeth – all in all, it's a wonder that kissing's supposed to be romantic at all, given the pitfalls. On the plus side, though, the reason kissing is so widely practised (there's probably some tribe somewhere who shake each other's ears, or suck eyebrows, or something, but I've never heard of them) is that there are hundreds of nerve-endings in your lips, all jangling for attention. And, of course, getting that close to somebody else's orifice is a deeply intimate thing to do. It may not feel intimate, when you're exploring a stranger's fillings at 2 a.m. outside the chip shop, but ideally, trust me, kissing should be. There are as many different ways to kiss as there are ways to have sex, though – so simply lunging in the general direction of his mouth, sticking your tongue in and swishing it about like a squee-gee mop won't suffice, I'm afraid. If you want to be a champion kisser, you need to concentrate. Here comes the science bit.

the perfect kiss

START SLOWLY

Most teenagers believe that snogging is a simple matter of pressing their open mouths together and rotating their heads anticlockwise. However, the more mature woman is fully aware that this kind of kissing leads only to an excess of spit, a numb jaw, and acute sexual boredom. Kissing by heading straight for an open mouth is like dispensing with foreplay and heading straight for open legs. It can work, but only if you want the sexual equivalent of a greasy takeaway – hot, fast, and you feel somehow cheated afterwards. Truly satisfying kissing begins nowhere near the lips – because ideally, by the time your mouths meet, you should already be melting with desire and longing. The best places to begin a kissing session are the cheekbone, or the neck. And best of all is the part of the neck situated just below your ear, which is more sensitive than a bullied jelly, and should respond to the feather-like touch of his lips by swamping you with sexual desire. Note use of the word 'feather-like'. If you're put in mind of a toothless pensioner eating an ice cream, you can reasonably expect that you will fail to be even slightly turned on. Assuming he gets that bit right, though – gentle grazing of lips along neck, light flickering of tongue below ear – then you'll soon be whimpering with passion. Then he should trail a series of gentle, tongue-free kisses along your cheek to the corner of your lips. Of course, he may not know this, having been brought up on films where the hero kills 15 baddies then bends the heroine backwards in the middle of the wreckage without bothering with all the ear-kissing stuff. So you can either explain to him that adrenaline does funny things to people, and the hero may be acting less sensitively than usual because he's just blown away a bunch of terrorists. Or, more simply, you can do it to him, and hope he gets the hint.

TONGUE – YES OR NO?

It's generally assumed that, once you progress to what you used to call 'French kissing' at school, you never look back. You assume closed-mouth kissing is for nervous 12-year-olds, and that you are now the Mistress of the Tongue. But before you start attempting to tie knots in cherry stalks with the tip, you should stop thinking of it as a kissing essential, and think of it as a delightful addition to the main action. Really, there's nothing worse than two people performing a tonsillectomy on each other with their tongues. It's not sensual, and after about five seconds it stops being even remotely enjoyable. Both parties simply end up thinking, 'Should I stop?', 'I need to swallow, but it'll make a funny noise', 'Did I brush my teeth?', and the whole thing falls apart. Instead, once you've reached the corner of his lips – or he's reached yours – exchange a few lingering kisses with your lips only. I don't mean pecking him like a Puritan granny at Christmas, obviously – slightly parted lips are perfectly desirable, so long as you've not been eating garlic and Roquefort pasta. But should he try to shove his tongue in, like a Labrador exploring an empty can of dog food, you'll need to back off a few inches to indicate that he's going a little too fast. When you return to his lips, make sure you're entertaining enough without using your tongue to make him realize that he's been missing out big-time.

LIP PLAY

The truth is, there are far more nerve-endings in your lips than in your tongue. So it makes sense that the best kisses will be lip-oriented. Hindu sex books in fact claim that women have a nerve that connects the upper lip to the clitoris. This may not be strictly true – otherwise, every time you bit your lip in deep thought, you'd have a violent orgasm – but the theory is valid. So, caressing each other's upper lips can be a deeply sensual experience. At this point, you can allow your tongues to run lightly around each other's mouths, before returning to butterfly-like lip-kissing. You may even wish to suck each other's bottom lips. If you do, however, try not to think about the Bushmen who have wooden plates inserted in their lower lips, because it's not the sexiest notion, and it might well make you laugh. You can try nibbling – gently, mind – on his lips, too, as this can stimulate all manner of nerve-endings he never knew he possessed. With luck, he'll cotton on to the idea, and reciprocate. But only when your lips are aflame with lust, as they say, should you progress to tongue-in-mouth action.

TONGUE PLAY

The key here is 'use sparingly'. It's no use creating this delicious soup of sexuality with all these delicate ingredients, if you're just going to chuck a big slab of meat in the pot at the end of it. As it were. So, once you've got past the lip-nibbling, mouth-kissing part, just flick your tongue gently into his mouth, and out again. Remember you're going for a 'sensual python' vibe, however, not a 'didn't-like-the-taste-so-came-straight-out' one. After a little more lip play, caress the inside of his lips with the tip of your tongue, and, no doubt, his own will soon venture out in response, like a shy woodland creature. Now, at this point it is entirely permissible to exchange saliva. You may, in fact, spend several seconds doing nothing but caressing each other's tongues. Just don't thrust them in so far you might choke. Always use the tip, in preference to the full length, and, as you mingle away, don't forget to alternate the position of your head, in order to avoid a stiff neck, and provide yet more sensitive pressure on different areas of your lips. A word of warning, however – don't wibble it around so much you keep bumping noses or, worse, resemble *Corrie*'s Deirdre Barlow and Mike Baldwin in the throes of their affair, when they were forced by cruel directors to snog like blind turtles seeking food.

As the kiss draws to a natural conclusion – and that'll happen around the time you stop being able to breathe without an oxygen mask – pull gently away, and kiss him once more on the lips before parting. Otherwise it's all a little too reminiscent of a sunken ship being airlifted to the surface, with accompanying plunging noises and damp aftermath.

where else to kiss

While Coco Chanel may have commented that she put perfume everywhere she liked to be kissed, there are certain spots on the body that may well require scent, but can do without kissing full stop. Namely, feet. Unless they are the most fragrant pair that ever walked on marabou-fluff slippers, and men generally beg to drink champagne from your discarded Manolos, don't try and force your man to kiss your feet. Because a) it's demeaning, b) it's not very pleasant, and c) you wouldn't want to kiss his.

Apart from that, you can be kissed absolutely anywhere and enjoy it. On a Nile barge ... up the Eiffel Tower ... in Las Vegas ... no, no, on the body, silly. Aside from the obvious erogenous zones, and we'll be dealing with those later on, almost every area of you has enough nerves to feel pretty nice when it's kissed. Of course, he'll have to be fairly comprehensive in his kissing to find the bits that truly turn you on, as opposed to the bits that you can take or leave. Some will feel more exciting that white-water rafting down Niagara Falls, while others will be marginally less interesting than a trip to the shops. Some will be pleasantly inbetween – the equivalent of watching *Friends* with a glass of wine, perhaps. And, although everyone's different, and one woman's sensuous arm-caressing may be another's irritating itch, there are some places he really should visit.

DOWN THE BACK

The back of your neck is a positive playground of nerve-endings. Your spine – he should kiss up and down its length as if he's play-ing arias on a flute. Or even 'Streets of London' on a recorder. The place where your spine curves into your bum – but you may get the giggles if he then proceeds to kiss you all over your buttocks, as they're often alarmingly ticklish. Of course, the backs of your thighs are a prime spot, and he should trail his lips down the inner sides, to have you whimpering and begging like a starving puppy. The backs of your knees are also extremely sensitive, and a little licking here won't go amiss. So when he's got you all of a-quiver, turn over and he can continue to drive you insane with giddy lust. Or, at any rate, it might feel quite nice.

UP THE FRONT

We've already discussed the vast erotic potential of the neck. Although, if your boyfriend has sharp incisors and an inexplicable dislike of sunlight, you might want to skip this bit. Instead, make him kiss your collarbone, and tease you by trailing kisses along the top of your breasts. He should kiss all around your nipples, but ignore them – there's nothing like anticipation for getting you thoroughly worked up. Some women are odd about their stomachs. Usually, their stomachs aren't odd at all, but if you're going to be lying there thinking, 'My god, I look like the Michelin man', you aren't going to feel wildly sexual, so he can skip that bit, and kiss your hipbones instead – the little hollow on the inside responds particularly well to friendly licking. Again, avoid the obvious – don't let him kiss anything furry (unless you happen to be a 1970s feminist with particularly sensual armpits). Your legs, strangely, are probably not as sensitive at the front as they are the back – but don't let that stop him trying.

And then, of course, he may kiss your hand in thanks. Not sexy, but rather chivalrous.

Finally, you may want him to kiss your face. It can all be a bit embarrassing, as you lie there wondering if you're breathing too loud, and he debates whether you're actually enjoying having your eyelids tickled – but if it turns you on, go for it. Just bear in mind that having your nose kissed is more teddy bear than sex goddess. The best way to have your face kissed, however, is very lightly, all over. And, for heaven's sake, shut your eyes – otherwise he'll look like a giant bug crawling over a camera lens.

eyes wide shut

Which brings us neatly to the question: Eyes shut or open during kissing? I'd recommend largely shut – with occasional glances to show that you know who he is. If you keep them open, it's far too easy to start analysing everything, and looking at your own body in a less than complimentary light. Just say to yourself, 'He wants to kiss it, he's happy', shut your eyes, and concentrate on the sensations, rather than the strange hair you've suddenly noticed on your left breast . If he's an eyes-open kind of a guy, don't feel you have to match him, stare for stare – you'll end up so busy checking out what's happening you won't notice how the kiss feels, just how his forehead wrinkles up weirdly when he gets passionate.

kissing him

Of course, you can't expect this seven-course banquet of oral affection without offering something in return. But the good news is, all you have to do is what you'd like him to do to you. The only two differences are, firstly, men don't usually have skin quite as sensitive as women's, so while you may be playing harmonies of love on his forearm, he may be mentally flipping through the sports pages and rolling his eyes. So be aware of his body language – if he isn't panting with lust, and writhing with desire, it may be that you can skip this part.

Secondly, he is genitally oriented. Which means that just because you're happy to have your neck caressed for three hours without sparing a thought for your clitoris, he may not be so detached. In fact, it's a dead cert he'll be attempting to thrust his willy into your hand the minute you've pecked his ear. So you'll have to be firm with him. On the plus side, you don't have to kiss him for nearly so long to get a result.

kissing during sex

You'd imagine that kissing during sex comes as naturally as forcing him into the wet patch afterwards. But you'd be wrong. The trouble is, it's all a bit too reminiscent of rubbing your tummy and patting your head at the same time – a nightmare of coordination. So it's fine while he's lying next to you, rubbing your bits and with his face at eye-level. But once you move into position for thrusting, it all goes horribly wrong. If you're on top, to kiss him you need to bend forward at an unnatural angle, and risk severing his penis. Not ideal. If he's on top, you can't possibly coordinate your snogging when he's moving back and forth like a piston, and you'll end up with a broken nose or cracked teeth if you're not careful. And, if you're doing it doggy-style, you'll have to spin your head round like Regan in *The Exorcist* to be in with even a chance of lip contact. The only position that is suitable for intercourse kissing is you on top, him sitting up – then your heads are on the same level, and you can grind around gently in his lap while you kiss. Whatever you do, don't even think about trying to kiss when you've got your legs up on his shoulders. You'll end up the shape of a paperclip, being carried into casualty by guffawing paramedics. On the bright side, you'll provide a fantastic anecdote for everyone else in the waiting area.

kissing tips

1. Always clean your teeth beforehand – if you don't have a toothbrush handy, chew some minty gum. But remember to take it out before he kisses you, eh?
2. Don't kiss with a cold sore – passing one on is the least classy thing in the world, second only to giving an acne-ridden sixth-former a lovebite and writing his name in a heart on the bus window.
3. Move your hands around while you kiss – I don't mean make shadow puppets, just make sure you caress his back, or squeeze his bum. Nobody wants to be locked in a wooden embrace while they snog.

4. If you don't want to go any further than kissing, keep your hands higher up than his shoulders – any slight descent might make him think you're heading south with a purpose in mind, leading to all sorts of difficult explanations.
5. If he's a crap kisser, and you're in despair, say, 'Can I tell you something? I love kissing you, and there's this way of kissing that drives me insane – would you try it?' Then show him what to do, and act insane when he does it. He'll be so proud of himself, he'll do it every time.

kisses to copy

1. Sandra Bullock and Keanu Reeves in *Speed* – train crash, bystanders, adrenaline – excellent!
2. Celia Johnson and Trevor Howard in *Brief Encounter* – restrained passion, desire fighting duty – erotic!
3. Gwyneth Paltrow and Joseph Fiennes in *Shakespeare in Love* – poetry, lust, danger of discovery – thrilling!

kisses to avoid

1. Tom Cruise and Kelly McGillis in *Top Gun* – tongues everywhere, pounding synth-rock – bad.
2. Michael Douglas and Sharon Stone, *Basic Instinct*. Old turtles with waving, crepey necks – alarming.
3. Mike and Deirdre in *Coronation Street* – creaking leather sofa, large glasses, too much noise – unappealing.

And finally, three kissing essentials – lip balm, toothbrush and breath freshener. OK?

oral sex

I regret to say that we of the FBI are powerless to act in cases of oral-genital intimacy, unless it has in some way obstructed interstate commerce.

J. Edgar Hoover

Of all the basically acceptable sex acts in all the world, oral sex probably causes the most worry and distaste. Either you're worried about having it done to you, in case you smell weird, your bits are strangely shaped, it's too wet, it's not wet enough, or he gets hairs caught in his teeth. Or you worry about doing it to him in case he smells weird, his bits are strangely shaped, it's too big, not big enough, or, far more troublingly, he'll choke you, or you'll embarrass him by spitting out the essence of his manhood and gasping, 'Christ, where's the water?' There is no more intimate act – many women will have sex with men they wouldn't shake hands with in daylight, but they wouldn't dream of putting his willy in their mouths, or letting him put his tongue on their bits. So, without wishing to sound like a tedious therapist, it's worth mentioning that the most important ingredient when it comes to oral sex is trust. If you don't trust him, you'll be as far from an orgasm as Mother Teresa in a cold shower, because you'll spend the entire time wondering what he's thinking, and whether he's secretly laughing at your clitoris, or gagging at your womanly scents. And if you're giving him a blowjob, you'll spend the time wondering whether he's thinking you're an easy lay, and will tell all his mates, or if he's merely suffering from some dreadful, symptomless sexual disease that you're about to catch. So it helps to know and like him before you venture into oral sex territory, to avoid all this pointless concern.

giving a blowjob

Q: What's the worst blowjob you've ever had?
A: Fantastic.

Not the subtlest joke in the world, but surely the truest. Ask any man if he'd rather have a blowjob from someone who doesn't know what she's doing, or a full-body massage from a Bangkok whore, and he'll go for option A every time. Basically, having his willy sucked and licked is most men's idea of heaven on earth – partly because it feels amazing, and partly because by showing that you're prepared to accept his penis so intimately, you demonstrate your total acceptance and admiration of his manly fineness. But, on the whole, he's just aware that it feels amazing. There are very few things you can actually do wrong – the only serious disaster is failing to tuck your teeth behind your lips. If you don't, your erotic floorshow will grind to a swift halt, as he rolls about, shrieking in agony, and you curl up and die quietly in the corner. Other than that, any mouth–penis action is good news as far as he's concerned. Why do you think he spends so long in bed trying to force your head downwards as if he's trying to duck you in a swimming pool? So the reassuring bit is, if you want to make him your grateful love-slave, all you have to do is lick and suck his willy for a while. If you want to make him your eternally grateful love-slave, who would crawl across broken glass just to bring you chocolates, however, you need to refine your technique a little.

the perfect blowjob

POLE POSITION

The most important thing, rather than any kind of showgirl tongue technique, is knowing what position to get into. If you start with your head twisted to one side, he'll be begging you not to stop, and within seconds you'll be getting buzzing in your ears from the suppressed blood-flow to your brain. Or lockjaw. The best position to start from is kneeling. I know it's all terribly anti-feminist and demeaning and all, but if you're going to do it, you may as well let him enjoy his Roman Emperor slave-girl fantasies fully, before you make him wash up later. Sit him on the edge of the bed, or chair, and take up your position between his knees. You shouldn't have to bend forward too far to reach his willy. Alternatively, he could stand – but his legs might well give way halfway through. If he prefers to lie down, your best bet is also to lie down with your head level with the relevant bits – but rather than lying on your stomach and getting a crick in your neck, lie on your side, place your head on his thigh, like a little cushion, and put his penis in your mouth from a sideways-on position. Cunningly, this not only gives your head support, it also allows the tip to bump against your cheek, rather than your tonsils – immediately cutting out any fears you may have of retching in an undignified fashion.

BALL PLAY

Before you proceed, bear in mind that a man with his most precious possession clamped between your jaws is in a vulnerable position, to say the least. So, rather than treating it like a Groucho Marx cigar, and sticking it in your mouth and waggling it around, you may want to show a degree of care and consideration for the whole area. Cup his balls gently in the palm of your hand, so you can stroke them with your thumb throughout. Don't, whatever you do, squeeze. At all. With the other hand, you have a choice. If you actually want him to come spectacularly, fairly swiftly, you should grasp the base of his penis firmly, and rub up and down the shaft in rhythm with your sucking movements. Getting him to come through oral sex alone can be difficult, as he requires a fairly significant pressure. On the other hand, if you just want to give him a trailer to the main action, use your spare hand to rub his chest, or stroke his back, or thighs – it's not like he'll notice – you could be building the Taj Mahal from matchsticks behind his back for all he'll care.

ORAL SEX

Begin by licking the tip of his penis. (I'm assuming it's already erect by now – if not, pop the whole thing in your mouth and suck till it expands magically.) Don't lap at it like a nervous kitten at a puddle – it isn't your clitoris, it likes stimulation that means something, not the mere suggestion of stimulation coupled with fantasies about firemen that you may favour. Use your tongue to lick big spirals, right around the top.

You can, if you wish, put just the head – or the glans – in your mouth, and imagine you're kindly keeping a bald man's head warm for him. Fasten your lips – that's lips, not teeth – around the ridge just below the head, hold the shaft with your hand, and manipulate it slowly up and down while you lick. In a surprisingly short while, his penis will start behaving like an overexcited salmon, leaping about in its desperation to get further into your little oral cave of wonders. At this point, you can either flex your jaw – gently – and keep him where he is. Or, you can go for the full *Deep Throat* experience, and slowly feed it in. Keep your lips closely round it – which prevents unsightly dribbling – and stop when it feels as if you're trying to win a hot-dog-eating competition. You can use your tongue to push it back to a manageable distance in your mouth. Then, move your head back and forth, keeping your lips well moistened.

Don't feel you have to keep going if your head's bobbing like a chicken and paralysis of the jaw is setting in – if he's begging you to carry on, use your shaft-hand to rub, whilst making lazy circles on the tip with your tongue. You can rest your neck, and it's not like he'll object. Initially, of course, you'll be going slowly – but as he gets increasingly beside himself, he'll want you to speed up. At this point, you have to make two decisions – 1) Am I prepared to keep going with my mouth till he comes, despite the potential exhaustion factor? and 2) Do I spit or swallow? With the first question, if you decide you can't take the neck pain, just leave your lips over the tip, and use your hand to rub like the well-oiled piston he's demanding. If you decide to do the decent thing and carry on using your mouth, make sure you're really comfortable before you get onto the fast bit. And don't worry about a bit of saliva getting on his thigh: he wouldn't care if it was liquid nitrogen by this stage. Question 2? Ah, now that's more awkward.

SPIT OR SWALLOW?

Unfortunately, this sort of thing was never covered in Victorian etiquette books. You may have no problems with swallowing any amount of semen he cares to produce – but if so, you're unusual. For most girls, the idea of knocking back bucketloads of bodily wallpaper paste is less appealing than eating raw oysters out of season. The good news is, it isn't really bucketloads – the average bloke produces about a spoonful. The taste depends on whether he eats meat or drinks a lot – it varies. But it generally tastes like nothing you'd want to eat on toast. Spicy wallpaper paste, perhaps.

There's also the fact that it's oddly warm, and hits the back of your throat like a splash-bomb. Then again, it's a truly intimate gesture to swallow what is, effectively, his very life-blood … just so long as you don't imagine all the sperm galloping down your throat, at any rate. Swallowing, however, is perfect bed etiquette. It makes him feel accepted and desired, and he'll appreciate your gesture immensely. You can tell when he's about to come, because his penis will suddenly swell alarmingly. So the trick is to tip your head back and swallow as soon as it hits – that way it goes straight down without touching your tongue, and you don't have to taste it. A big glass of wine by the bed helps enormously – it'll wash away any lingering aftertaste, particularly if you want to kiss him straight away.

Spitting is altogether more fraught with difficulties – chief amongst them being the sheer rudeness of gobbing out his precious fluids on the duvet. Imagine how you'd feel, if he sat up from orally giving you a shuddering orgasm and then spat into a tissue. Nice.

So you must be subtle. Most men are fully aware that seminal fluid is not the tastiest dish in the land. So if you ask him to warn you when he's about to come, if he's any kind of gentleman, he will. It may take the form of 'Arghmmmf yeah, oh, mmmf', but at least you'll get some idea that it's imminent. At this point, you can either remove your mouth altogether – in which case, a kind gesture would be to let him come all over your chest, so he feels like a German porn star. Or you can catch it in your mouth, turn to one side, and spit it – silently – into a tissue. Don't make the kind of hawking noise that 13-year-old lads at bus stops make when they spit, if you want him to be happy with your decision. And afterwards, make sure you're very complimentary. 'It felt so big' should do the trick nicely – like I said, it's not rocket science.

FANCY TECHNIQUES

Of course, the above blowjob is more than enough fun for most men. But if you really want a diploma in advanced stimulation skills – perhaps you've both been taken hostage, and it's the only entertainment you'll get for the next five years – there are certain techniques that will make the time simply fly by. For him, at least. You'll just emerge into the sunlight of freedom with a jawline like Bruce Forsyth and a permanent stoop. Still, they're tricks worth knowing if you want to be a true oral goddess.

The flicker

If you weren't brought up by snakes, you won't know how good this can be. Basically, hold the shaft in one hand, and flick your tongue, fast then slowly, right alongside the vein that runs up the front of his erect penis. Don't press on it; just use your flickering tongue to caress the length.

The swirl

See that ridge just under the head of his penis that goes right round? Well, it responds very well to attention. Run your tongue round it, then wiggle it up and down on the frenulum – which is the bit that joins the head to the shaft at the front. It's extremely sensitive, so pay it some attention.

The full monty

Insert his penis in your mouth (possibly a contender for Every Man's Favourite All-Time Phrase) and, whilst sucking lightly, moving your mouth up and down the shaft, use your tongue to caress the head, and your hand to rub the base. He might die, though.

The hot and cold job

For the braver man. Some sexperts suggest you use a chilli, but I can't think why you would unless you had a grudge against him. Instead, take a drink of warm tea or coffee, and keep it in your mouth. Push his willy in, without spilling any, and swirl it around. Then, while he's reeling from that sensation, have a quick suck on an ice lolly, and plunge him back in. He won't know whether he's coming or going. But it's probably coming. You can also try it with champagne, for an exciting bubble-inspired thrill.

Eat and lick

One for the peckish girl. Simply arrange the foodstuff of your choice on his erect penis – though a selection of fruits, or choco-late, is more suitable than roast beef and Yorkshire pudding – and eat it, or lick it off. Good foods include half-strawberries, tangerine segments, mango, custard, whipped cream and chocolate buttons. Bad ones include lager, pies, peas and baked potatoes. But you probably already knew that.

oral sex for you

It'd be a dismal shame to avoid letting him go down on you because you're worried he won't like the way you smell/look/ taste. The truth is, most men adore the taste of ladies' bits, because they're programmed to want to get as close as possible. If you wash, there's no reason to be concerned – and certainly don't bother with those hygiene-obsessed deodorant sprays, because they'll make him feel he's making love to a bottle of toilet cleaner.

The only real worry you have is that most men don't have a clue what's going on down there – he can locate the clitoris, perhaps, but he certainly doesn't know what kind of pressure it requires. So you must let him know – either by telling him, or by moving about till you're in a position where he can't get it wrong.

Most women respond best to circular tongue movements on their clitorises (or should that be clitori?) He doesn't need to press too hard, though, or his tongue will wear out before he's begun properly. Make sure he keeps it gentle – and, most importantly, keeps it rhythmic. There's nothing worse than a fantastic build-up that's suddenly ruined because he stopped to change position. Once it's working, tell him, he has to carry on. He can alternate with flicking the top of his tongue over the whole labial area – a particularly spectacular move – but try to avoid letting him embark on series of dog-like licks. It doesn't work, and you'll feel ridiculous.

He may want to thrust his tongue up your vagina. Feel free – but pushing it in and out will be as much use as trying to hot-wire a car with a hairbrush. It needs to be a much more delicate operation, involving circular, 'key-unlocking' movements, coupled with a finger on your clitoris at the same time. Yes, it's complicated, alright?

He may also like the idea of blowing on you – but, if so, tell him in no uncertain terms not to blow hard up your vagina, unless he wants to give you an embolism that will kill you shortly afterwards. He should, in fact, keep all his touches light, until you're so turned on you're convinced you might explode.

At that point, he can intensify the pressure of his tongue, and make sure he maintains it till you orgasm.

If you have trouble disassociating yourself from feeling stupid and exposed as you look down at him sporting a curly beard and periodically sniffing, encourage him to move his hands around as well. Specifically, to move them onto your breasts, and caress your nipples lightly between a finger and thumb as he licks. It may require a miracle of coordination, but it's an almost guaranteed orgasm for you.

FANCY TRICKS

Three-point turn

If he can get his tongue on your clitoris, one finger inside you, and another pressing on your perineum – or even anus – you should be awash with sensation. But it's important that he keeps the rhythm and pressure the same in each area – otherwise you'll just feel confused.

Hot/cold

It's not quite so easy to turn you on with the hot/cold business as it is for him – because you have a much higher chance of your inner workings being irritated by whatever substances you use. Try champagne, but if you're sensitive the acidic bubbles might actually hurt. And don't ever, ever, use spirits, like brandy, even in your most rock 'n' roll excesses. Sore? And then some. Ice, too, will be less erotic, more agonizing. But you'll be OK with a nice cup of tea.

Food

Again, the foods that work for his penis will work for you up to a point – but you don't want to imbalance the flora and fauna of your vagina. Honey is fine, being naturally sterile, and washed fruit shouldn't pose a problem. Anything with pesticides, or chemicals and additives, however, should be avoided. So no putting jelly sweeties or Chinese takeaways up yourself, OK?

Face-sitting

Sitting on his face is a very porn-star thing to do, if you can overcome the terror of that garlic you ate last week coming back to haunt you at an inopportune moment. But if you do it, make sure you have something to hold onto. Otherwise, your thighs will be in severe pain, from holding you up at the point of orgasm. Or else, he'll suffocate. And, knowing you, you'll be so carried away you won't even notice.

Holding it apart

This is not a tip for the retiring nun. However, if he's having trouble getting to your clitoris, you can help him along by holding your labia apart with a finger and thumb, thus exposing it neatly. Also, the pressure of your hand, and the newly raised position of the clitoris which makes it all the easier to stimulate, will enhance your orgasm no end.

things not to do

YOU TO HIM

1. Don't listen to sex advice which tells you to hum whilst giving a blowjob. It doesn't afford much vibration, and, more importantly, you'll feel a complete prat.
2. Don't attempt to be a vixen by playfully nibbling his balls. He will probably knee you in the stomach with shock, then insist you drive him to hospital.
3. Don't try and swallow if you really hate it. There's nothing even faintly sexy about running to the toilet gagging afterwards.

HIM TO YOU

1. He shouldn't continue when you're obviously bored – 'obviously bored' signals include sighing, throat-clearing, or shifting hips aimlessly to and fro in a bid to get turned on. Teach him when to give up.

2. He shouldn't expect you to orgasm as fast as he does – which is why 69 is such a useless position. It's just confusing, because he's coming like an express train, while you're more like a scenic steam engine to Aberystwyth.

3. He shouldn't lift his chin to pick hairs out of his teeth, or wipe his mouth ostentatiously when he's finished. And he certainly shouldn't ever break off to say, 'Are you nearly there? My jaw's numb.'

Manual matters

I've tried several varieties of sex. The conventional position makes me claustrophobic and the others give me a stiff neck or lockjaw.

Tallulah Bankhead

There are times when you don't want to bother with the time-consuming nature of full sex. Maybe you've got your period; maybe you're just tired; possibly, you'd simply like to watch *Ally McBeal* uninterrupted. And these are the times when knowing what to do with your hands is invaluable. Giving the perfect handjob is one of the easiest sexual activities you can perform – men are, as we know, simple creatures biologically, and, while getting him to fiddle with your bits satisfactorily is a far more complex job, not unlike changing a plug in the dark, bringing him to orgasm is often as easy as switching the light on. Well, almost.

The only talents you require are a firm grip and a strong wrist – if yours is rather weak, practise by unscrewing the tops of jam jars. He may wonder why you're acting like a stalwart of the Women's Institute, but once you explain he's unlikely to argue.

Of course, it's not just his penis (and believe me, there is no better word for it, because I've tried for years to find one. 'Willy' makes you sound about three, 'dick' is just silly, and 'cock' makes you sound like a Vegas hooker. Then again, some men may like that ...) Your hand is also useful for stimulating all his little erogenous areas – which, in men, tend to be clustered intimately around the penis. His balls, for example, which are often demoted to the position of 'penis's handbag – good for carrying sperm, but not worth bothering with'. Or the perineum, an unwieldy word for the neat little bit that joins his balls and bum. Or even his bum itself – just so long as it's cleaner than a nun's mind, obviously. In fact, that goes for everywhere you might touch: if it doesn't smell more fragrant than morning dew on a rose (or at least, Insignia shower gel on a willy) don't bother at all. And you can tell him that from me.

the perfect handjob

A lot of women get very intimidated at the idea of administering a handjob. They think they're going to do it wrong somehow – they worry they might hurt him, or use the wrong speed, or the wrong pressure ... but in fact it's so easy to get right you may as well save your worrying for your own orgasm, which offers far more pitfalls. Of course, you must be guided by his sighs, gasps and general comments – if he says 'Yes... oh! Oh, God! Yes!' you're probably doing it right. Whereas if he shouts, 'No! in the name of God, woman, what are you playing at?' you could have gone wrong somewhere. Some men don't speak at all, they just stare fixedly at a point on the opposite wall, with their eyes bulging like Marty Feldman's. If he's doing that, though, he's probably happy, so don't interrupt him.

Once you've kissed for a while, trail your hand down his chest and stomach – you can take as long over this as you want, but he probably knows (or hopes) what's next, so don't waste too much time drawing intricate finger-patterns on his torso if you'd rather get on with it. It's often helpful to use some lubrication at this stage, if you're not overly familiar with his penis – otherwise, you risk getting pubic hairs, or folds of skin, trapped between your fingers, and bringing tears to his eyes. KY jelly, if you can bring yourself to walk into the chemist's and buy it, is the best type – perhaps you could say loudly, as you join the queue, 'Honestly, I can't believe my best friend is so uptight she has to get me to do her personal shopping for her.' Alternatively, you can order lubricants from sex-shop catalogues – a particularly fine one is called 'Probe'. What could be sexier? If not, use saliva (mmm!), or even body oil, so long you aren't planning to use condoms afterwards – oil will rot them.

THE GRASP

Now, grasp his erect penis with your right hand (or left, obviously, if you're left-handed). You should make a fist shape round the shaft, using your whole hand, with your thumb at the top. All your fingers and palm should be in contact with his skin, and the head should be poking out like a curious meercat. Don't make the mistake of assuming it's like your clitoris, and you must be delicate. No man wants his penis held like a china teacup, with your little finger sticking out. Don't squeeze, but hold it as you'd hold a half-pint glass – firmly enough to prevent spilling any or dropping it, but not hard enough to break the glass. Now, move your hand up and down. Simple, isn't it? Keep to a steady rhythm, slowly at first, and make sure you pull the foreskin right over the head and back again. If he's circumcised (i.e. no foreskin), move your hand up over the head anyway, as this is the most sensitive part. Do not, under any circumstances, pull, tweak or wrench – an erect penis is robust yet vulnerable, and a sudden lurch could be agonizing. As you rub, kiss and caress him too; otherwise he's going to feel like he's paying by the hour and there's a queue forming outside. As he gets more excited – you can tell because his penis will get bigger, and he'll make noises (unless he's the bug-eyed type, in which case he'll just stare harder) – speed up your movements, but keep them rhythmic. When he's about to come, go as fast as you can manage – it may become excessively tiring after a while, so if he's taking ages you can return to slow, then go back to fast, to give your wrist a rest – which is unbearably exciting for him, as an added bonus. If you've got stamina, though, you should find that he'll have a spectacular orgasm – all over your hand and himself, so have some tissues handy. The true sex goddess may wish to bend down and swallow it as it arrives – but if you don't, no one's going to blame you.

Don't whisk your hand away as soon as he starts to ejaculate. That kind of abandonment suggests you're thinking, 'By God, that's revolting. I'll have to get these sheets in the washer', and isn't a very sensual move. Keep it round his penis, but relax your grip, and tease out three or four gentle strokes, till he's finished. And try not to leap to your feet, scrubbing violently at yourself with tissues – discreet wiping is all that's required.

ADVANCED TECHNIQUE

The basic handjob would keep most men happy on a desert island for several years. But if you really want to impress him, you may wish to try out a few advanced techniques. There are certain sex manuals that explain these moves with enough diagrams, sub-divisions and arrows to make the whole thing look more complicated than fixing a dodgy carburettor, but it's really not that difficult, and you don't need diagrams or a safety net to do them. Just a hand and a decent sense of rhythm.

The twist

You definitely need lubrication for this one, to prevent him getting his skin all twisted and painful. So coat both hands generously in it, and, starting at the base of the shaft, grasp his penis, and then twist – think jam jars again. Move slowly upwards, then begin with your other hand, making the same movements. Try to keep them flowing, rather than jerky – and, when you reach the top, caress the head with your thumb, and move downwards again. Keep this up till he's whimpering foolishly; then, if you want him to come, switch to the basic method.

The anemone

You know how sea anemones wave their fronds seductively underwater? Well, that's you. Place your palms against his penis, so he feels all warm and enclosed. Join your fingers together over the head, and then simply flex them in and out, in frond-like fashion, so you're caressing the head with all your fingers, and the movement of your palms is stimulating the shaft. He will feel like a little fish being stroked in the undersea world ... Alternatively, he'll just feel damned excited – although his penis is built to withstand thrusting, it also likes the gentle touch now and then, too.

The semi-shag

This is the ultimate handjob tip for lazy girls. All you have to do is fill your palms with KY or similar, and make a big hollow fist by lacing your fingers together, and leaving an opening between your thumbs. Then, you simply lie there dozing, while he thrusts in and out of it to his heart's content. No effort, for maximum turn-on. Don't you wish you had a willy?

The breast job

Well, it's not strictly manual. But for those of you whose dream job is 'German porn star', it's certainly worth trying. All you have to do is squeeze your breasts together, then let him insert his penis between them and thrust away. No effort on your part, but you will feel as if Ben Dover should be directing the scene. This may be a good or a bad thing. A warning, though – either make him wear a condom, or be prepared for the fact that you're going to get semen in your face and, probably, hair. Porn!

balls

It's all too easy to neglect the balls, dangling away there as if they're nothing to do with him. But they are, in fact, highly sensitive little sacs of pleasure, and if you're bothering to stimulate his penis you may as well throw a ball or two in there as well. The most important thing to remember when it comes to balls is: never – ever – squeeze or press them. If the penis is an SS commando with a sensitive side, then the balls are new recruits in the barracks, crying themselves to sleep at night, when it comes to being easily hurt.

The good news is, you can do pretty much anything you like as long as you're gentle. Think of them as the male equivalent of breasts, and you won't go far wrong. It's best if you fondle them in tandem with willy-fondling – if you concentrate on them alone, he may become rather frustrated, because it feels great, but he isn't going to orgasm through balls alone. There are certain touches, however, that work with or without penis-pressing.

There's a line up the centre of the balls – and it leads to their most sensitive part, the bit of skin that joins them to the penis. If you run your tongue along the line, and then flick it lightly on the join, he should feel pretty happy. He also likes to have them cradled in your hands, and stroked with your fingers. Then again, if you're got a big mouth (and surely that's been mentioned before now) you can go for the ultimate ball-experience, which is to insert them both in your mouth and run your tongue all over them. Alright, yes, they may be hairy and wrinkled. But Catherine Zeta Jones went and married Michael Douglas, so surely you can cope with that.

the perineum

This is not a submarine-tracking device, or an ancient Greek temple, as you may suspect. It is, more boringly, the joining-bit between arse and balls. And, because the highly sensitive urethra is positioned just above it, and the prostate not far off, it feels very nice indeed when touched. Don't, as a friend of mine once did, prod your finger into it as if you're trying to unblock a sink. The guy in question remained a one-night stand, funnily enough. But do use a firm pressure to stroke or lick it – coupled with a hand-job, this is a memorable addition.

the anus

Oh dear, we had to get to it sooner or later. So those of you who find the idea of sticking a finger up their boyfriend's bum both repulsive and alarming may wish to take a short break now. Those who don't, however, read on.

You may have heard of the male G spot. This is just a fancy sex-manual word for the prostate gland, which is rather like a small grape, and has remarkable power to intensify orgasm. Unfairly, women don't have one at all, which is why gay men have so much fun with anal sex, but women tend to feel like a resentful Christmas turkey being stuffed with garlic and sage. So, if you can insert your finger into his anus – it may help to dress as a nurse at this point – you'll be able to reach the prostate, which is situated towards his balls. It feels smooth, but you'll know when you've reached it because he'll shriek with excitement. Just rub your fingertip lightly on it – ideally, whilst stimulating his penis – and your reward will be his eternal devotion. If you don't fancy the full potholing experience, you can still give him great pleasure stroking a finger on his arsehole, without venturing in. It's very sensitive, and will add to any experience he may be enjoying – unless he's in a meeting with his boss, of course. Needless to say, keep your nails short, go slowly, and use lubrication – again. Honestly, at this rate, you'll be keeping KY in business. You could always tell the chemist you're a cross-channel swimmer and you need it for thermal insulation.

what about you?

So you've explored every manual possibility. Now it's your turn. And your plumbing is a tad more complex than the grasp-and-rub techniques used on him. So first, a quick map. Starting at the top – from the bikini line down.

Between the folds of labia – and that is not, admittedly, the most charming phrase for what is essentially a fantastic feat of technical engineering – you should find, first off all, your clitoris, covered with a little flap of skin. It feels like a very small pea –

only obviously, more sensitive. Moving on, you'll find your urethra – a small hole like a Tiny Tears doll's wee-hole, which can't possibly be mistaken for a vagina, despite your worries. Then, of course, the remarkably elastic vagina entrance, capable of opening and closing like the cave in the *Arabian Nights*, according to how turned on you are. And then your own perineum, followed by, what else, your anus. So many bits, enclosed by protective yet sensitive folds. No wonder he gets confused.

CLITORAL FUN

It's incredible how many women put up with inept manhandling of their clitoris, simply because they're too polite to say anything. So men fumble away as if they're shammying a window, and their long-suffering partners lie there, bored and uncomfortable, too polite to shout, 'For Christ's sake I'm a woman not a starter motor.' And indeed, that could be upsetting for him. All the same, he probably needs a little help. Otherwise, you're doomed to be lying there, squeaking in pain and discomfort while he prods about like a junior doctor after a 22-hour shift. It's amazing, though, how few women actually understand their own bits and their responses – so we'll be covering masturbation later, for all those who think a vibrator is really for muscular aches and pains, like it says on the box.

But when he's got his hand down there, and is stroking caringly but ineptly, it helps to be able to guide him a little. And if telling is difficult, showing is very easy indeed – just gently move his hand to where you want it, and gasp with pleasure the moment he does the right thing. All men want to think they're some kind of Latino love god, and he'll be only too happy to continue if you give him the slightest encouragement. He should start off gently caressing your pubic mound (I know it sounds like an Anglo-Saxon burial site, but there's simply nothing else you can call it) with his whole hand, before he slips a finger down to your clitoris. Once located, he shouldn't press too hard – if he does, simply shift your hand wordlessly to the side, and murmur 'A bit softer?' in an adoring fashion. The big mistake men make is in assuming that the clitoris is like a mini-penis. Because, while the penis can take a fairly firm hand, as it were, your clitoris is more of a gentle flower that needs care and sensitivity before it can blossom as it should ... so, while he may be tempted, once you start gasping, to increase the pressure, he really should resist that urge. Nor should he change hands, alter the speed at which he's stroking, or generally bugger about in the hope of improving your fun. It's vital, in fact, that he sets up a regular rhythm, of either stroking in circles, or flicking lightly back and forth, and keeps it up. When you're very obviously on the verge of coming – (shouting 'Don't stop, don't stop' and shuddering like a horse after a 10 mile gallop) he can increase the speed a tiny bit. But not the pressure. In fact, you may want to draw up some diagrams for him to examine at leisure.

NIPPLE FUN

Your personal pleasure may well be increased if he touches – or licks – your nipples at the same time as he's fiddling with your clitoris. If he can coordinate himself, the Three-Point Turn is mind-blowing. He just has to reach an arm round your back to your far nipple, whilst dipping his head to lick the near one, and caressing your clitoris with his spare hand. He may require arms like Mr Tickle, but the resulting orgasm's infinitely worth any muscular pain it may involve for him. Importantly, he must keep the nipple-stroking rhythmic – there's nothing worse than flicking one whilst sucking the other, it's simply confusing. And he should never, ever, twiddle as if he's trying to tune into a pirate radio station 10 miles offshore. Nor should he suck so hard your delicate nipples make that unappealing popping sound when they emerge from his vacuum-like mouth. There's no faster turn-off than your own body emitting comedy noises. Gentle pulling, stroking or circling with his finger and thumb should be satisfactory – and don't let him forget about the rest of your breasts as well.

THE G SPOT

Many brave couples have attempted to locate the G spot armed only with Kendal mint cake and a torch, and returned, hours later, dispirited and confused. Basically, the damn thing was only discovered last century, by a Dr Graftenberg (hence 'G' spot – he's possibly the only man to have lent his name to a sexual zone; there aren't many Professor Clitorises around). So, if you have trouble finding it, it's not surprising. The idea is, though, that it's a little kidney-bean-shaped pad of flesh on the inner wall of your vagina. Nothing shaped like a kidney bean sounds very erotic, but bear with me. It's made of erectile tissue, which means that when it's stimulated, in theory, it feels much like a 14-year-old boy feels when confronted with a picture of Liz Hurley in a transparent bikini. The only problem is, if you are lucky enough to find it, he needs very long fingers in order to manipulate it. He could try flicking a fingertip across it, or rubbing in small circles. He certainly won't be licking it unless he's got a tongue like a giraffe. And, as giraffes' tongues are black and at least a foot long, that's not a terribly pleasing thought. G-spot-reaching positions include you on all fours, him behind you, with his fingers pointing forwards – or you lying down on your back, legs akimbo, while he explores with one finger at a time. If you can't find it, don't give up – there are always vibrators designed for that very purpose. Just don't wave your new purchase in his face, sniggering 'Hah, call yourself a man?' while all 12 inches buzz past his nose, as he may be feeling vaguely inadequate.

ANAL THINGS

Plenty of people don't even like to acknowledge that they have an anus, let alone come to terms with the idea that someone else might want to touch it. Admittedly, it takes a little getting used to – but, for some, it's deeply erotic to have such a forbidden area stimulated, by gentle stroking. Most women, it has to be said, don't feel a whole lot if a bloke shoves his finger up there – because we haven't got a prostate gland, so there aren't the fairground-ride thrills that he can experience on offer to us.

Preferable is the light stroking movement of his finger at the entrance, as it's fairly sensitive round there. But make sure you've washed first – because, if you're paranoid, you'll enjoy it about as much as an enema. Perhaps the Ferrari of stimulation is to have his fingers spanning your clitoris, vagina and anus – circling lightly on the clitoris, inserted a couple of centimetres into the vagina, and stroking the anus. But, if he isn't a Russian acrobat, get him to practise doing one thing at a time. It'll almost certainly be worth it.

positions

Those who restrain desire do so because theirs is weak enough to be restrained.

William Blake

The *Kama Sutra* has a lot to answer for. It may have been OK for ancient Hindus who'd practised yoga all their lives and consequently had bodies that painlessly bent like pretzels in pursuit of orgasm. But nowadays, all that 'two ducks flying past a goat' business simply serves to make the average reader feel inadequate, stiff-jointed and frankly rather dull. This is not the case at all – the simple truth is, there's no point torturing yourself into a position where your ankles are round your neck and your boyfriend's thighs are supporting your pelvis, or whatever – because you won't enjoy the sex, you'll just be thinking 'Ow', and 'I feel stupid' and 'I really hate the way my flab rolls into tyres when I crunch myself up'. In all honesty, there's only about five sexual positions worth bothering with – the rest are all simply decorative, or useful if you fancy seeing the world from a different perspective. The ideal positions to have sex in are, of course, ones which suit both you and him equally – and, remarkably, that is indeed possible.

mish posish

Let's assume for the sake of argument that you're having sex in bed. It's the obvious place – it's comfy, flat, and you aren't likely to fall off it in mid-thrust. It also the most versatile when it comes to positions. Obviously, you'll have been rolling around prior to the actual sex bit – and what tends to happen is, because he's programmed to want to impregnate you, at some point you will find that he's somehow rolled on top of you. Which is why missionary is such a useful position. It has fallen out of favour over the years, with women's magazines turning their noses up at the dullness of the mish – so called because when Christian missionaries went into the jungle, they taught the natives that it was the only respectable sexual position. Though what they were doing watching them copulate frantically is anybody's guess. Luckily, while it might be respectable, it's also fantastic – those Christians had to have something to keep them going through the long dark nights.

It works for most shapes and sizes – though if he's a 16 stone bullock and you're a seven stone ballerina, it's going to be difficult, and you may wish to skip to 'woman on top' for your jollies. Normally, though, it's perfect for women, because you get to lie on your back, lazy as you like, while he does all the hard work. You also get the rampant sexiness of full-body contact, you can kiss – though not when he's thrusting, as you'll just bang your teeth together like bad percussionists – and you get the opportunity to grab his bum as and when the mood takes you. And all you have to do is part your legs so he can angle himself in, like a rocket docking with the mother ship.

However, if you aren't the same height, you may have the problem that, even with your pelvis tilted upwards towards him, he can't get fully inside you. So shove a pillow under your bum, and you'll find it adds the extra height you need, and presents your entire vagina as an easy-to-enter tunnel. In this position, his thrusting should reach your G spot – if you believe in them – and if he grinds his hips, as well as thrusting, he may even be able to stimulate your clitoris. If his pelvis and your clitoris don't match up, however, that's perfectly normal – you may find that fully parting your legs (where's that German porn director when you need him?) exposes it enough to give it some stimulation – though some women prefer to keep their legs as close together as possible, so he's pressing on the whole pubic area when he thrusts upwards. If you're really serious about this clitoral-stimulation-during-sex thing, though, you can take it a step further and try the CAT position. So, you crouch over a saucer of milk, while he scratches your back ... no, just kidding. All will be explained.

THE COITAL ALIGNMENT POSITION (CAT)

Get into the normal missionary position – by the way, you're going to have to remember this, because you have no chance of making it work if you're waving this book around over his shoulder while you struggle into position. Once he's inside you, you stay still with your legs as close together as possible and he slowly moves up your body, until you're pelvis-to-pelvis. He may panic because he'll think his willy's going to bend backwards. It isn't – he just needs to get to the point where his pelvic bone is pressing on your clitoral area. And then, instead of leaping around like a rabbit peppered full of buckshot, he's going to grind his hips, very slowly, against you. You will find yourself grinding back, whether you intend to or not – and if you keep going, you are very likely to have a stupendous orgasm with him inside you, which for a surprising number of women, is a first. If it's not working first time, throw in a bit more lubrication and keep trying – just make sure you don't rub so hard your pubic hair bursts into flames.

MISSIONARY VARIATIONS

The beauty of the Mish is, it can be adapted to a number of positions, all of which provide slightly different stimulation, and all of which, rather brilliantly, involve you lying on your lazy arse.

Trussed chicken

Alright, it's my own name for it. But you can call it The Congress of The Water Buffalo all you like, and you'll still look like an oven-ready fowl. Despite that, pulling your legs up so your feet are on his chest (take your stilettos off first, darling, for God's sake) offers a range of sensations for both of you that makes the indignity worthwhile. He should kneel up – and you'd better have the light on for this one, because he doesn't want to miss when he's trying to get inside you. He'll have to lean forward, so his hands can range everywhere, but (particularly usefully), over your breasts and clitoris. This is a huge turn-on for him because he can see it all happening – this is why men spend a fortune on porn, because they absolutely love seeing close-ups of genitals engaged in sex. I know to us it can be about as sexy as seeing woodlice copulate, but let him have his fun – because the sensitive entrance to your vagina will be stimulated by his thrusting, when you're in this position, and your G spot will be doing cartwheels with gratitude. Three warnings, though:

a) don't expect to stay in this position a long time – however fit you are, at some point you're going to need to breathe properly

b) make sure his thrusting is gentle, or he's liable to fall out

c) don't think about what you might look like, whatever you do, or you'll have a vision of flab that'll put you off completely. He certainly isn't thinking about that, trust me on this.

Wrap-around

Easier to accomplish, the wrap-around is one for couples deep in lurve, because it gives you a feeling of total security. Look, I only said a feeling – he could be sleeping with your mother on the quiet for all I know, but it's nice while it lasts. And you just do what it says on the tin – wrap your legs around his back, so you're pulling him in towards you with every stroke. If you combine this with the bum pillow, you get the deepest penetration possible, so make sure he isn't banging away at your cervix, because it doesn't exactly hurt, but it feels funny. It's also a fantastic position for getting pregnant in, so watch yourself if that's not the intention. But, on the plus side, you get full-body contact, and, if you're really, sickeningly in love, you won't know where he ends and you begin. If you're not, though, it's still pretty nice – and cheer up, your mother probably can't get her legs to bend that far.

Spread-eagle

Again, it couldn't be simpler – you just open your legs as wide as they'll go. Try and do it when he's already inside you, though – otherwise he's just going to want to have a good look and possibly take pictures, and you'll start feeling like some kind of educational geographical phenomenon, rather than a red-hot sex-chick. So, once he's entered you, just stretch them out, either lying flat or sticking up in the air, and you'll find that suddenly your whole genital area feels sensitized, because you've opened out the protective folds, and exposed the most sensitive bits to sunlight. Or, at least, to his touch. It also helps him find your elusive clitoris, which can only be a bonus – and he's turned on because you're doing that amazingly sexy thing he honestly thought only girls in magazines did.

girls on top

Sometimes, despite its pleasures, the Mish just won't do for the sort of rampant vixen you fancy yourself as. And also, he might eventually complain about the fact that he's doing all the work. Plus, the basic missionary position doesn't provide great access to your tits – or your bits, come to that. So that's when you need to unpack your stetson and get on top. Never worry that he might not like this – the only man who might object is one who believes it's a woman's job to procreate, and to do that she should lie still, in the dark, until the whole messy and unpleasant business is over. And you really aren't likely to be having sex with your old headmaster, are you? So, allow him to lie on his back – and he doesn't have to do anything with pillows, he'll be pleased to note – and simply climb on top. Some men like to grab their willy and find the entrance themselves – others prefer it if you guide it in for them, and, in all honesty, this is infinitely easier because you know exactly where it's going – he doesn't. Don't make the novice's mistake, however, of thinking you'll just lower yourself straight onto it – you'll miss, it'll bend, and you'll end the encounter apologizing like you've just sold him a faulty lock.

Once inserted, he'll gasp with excitement, and hopefully it'll feel OK to you too. If it's painful, you're probably sitting too far back so it's pressing against your vaginal wall – so shuffle forward a bit, and then you can start to move. Don't make the mistake of starting too fast – if he takes a while to come, you'll feel like an Olympic sprinter, gasping for breath and trying to ignore the stitch in your side as you approach the final lap. The obvious movement is a back-and-forth piston move, which is fairly easy on the hips. Don't be too violent (his willy's in a vulnerable position here) but as you build up a head of steam, as it were, you can move up and down faster, so you're plunging the whole length of your vagina down onto his penis. Don't let it come out altogether, though – keep a couple of inches inside you, to avoid it falling out again. If that's a bit 'ride 'em cowgirl' for your delicate sensibilities, then just grind. Grinding is underrated in the bedroom, but it has the ability to reach the parts that thrusting simply can't reach. Move your hips in a clockwise motion – or a figure of eight, if you're feeling particularly coordinated and want to drive him crazy with lust. The beauty of this manoeuvre is it's not tiring, and it stimulates your clitoris an absolute treat.

There is, though, a move that you really should master if you want to have an earth-shattering orgasm whilst balanced on your man. The only problem is, again, it's not terribly dignified – but frankly, who cares, with this kind of pay-off? Instead of kneeling, you have to squat, with a foot on either side of his hips, and lower yourself directly onto his penis, with it sticking straight up like a flagpole (or a chipolata, depending). This is G-spot heaven, but it's knackering on your thigh muscles – and it helps if you wear high heels. So, with your hands resting lightly on his stomach for support, move up and down, making sure he remains sticking upright, and keeping your back straight – if you lean forward, the angle changes and the whole G-spot thing falls apart. But if you can keep going, you will be pleasantly amazed at the sensations you've created – plus, of course, he can always play with your nipples to help things along, should they need it. Some women (though I'm not one of them) swear by the reverse-on-top position. Which is simply, you sit on him, but facing his feet. It may well stimulate your nerve-endings to an impressive level, and the sight of your gyrating arse is good news for him – but your own visual stimulation's gone right out the window, quite frankly – it's not that easy to get turned on looking at a pair of bony, gnarled feet. Besides, the plus of you on top is the amount of access it gives your hands, not to mention his. You can reach round behind you and stroke his balls, squeeze his thighs, twiddle his nipples, and even lean forward and kiss him if the fancy takes you. Whilst he can, of course, play with your breasts, and stroke your clitoris – though he may not be terribly well coordinated as orgasm approaches. Alternatively, if you're an upfront kind of gal, you can do it yourself, thus ensuring an orgasm. But that really would be giving him an easy ride.

doggy-style

Now it starts getting tricky. You see, doggy-style – that's you on your hands and knees, him behind you, as opposed to you running to catch frisbees and shaking mud all over him – can be a bit of a psychological problem for some women. Mainly because there's something ever so slightly subservient about the idea of letting him take you from behind so he can't even see your face. There's always the fear that he might be mentally projecting Angelina Jolie's features onto your head, not to mention superimposing Jennifer Lopez's breasts over your own fried eggs. And then there's the fact that it isn't a terribly loving position, and if he did want to use and abuse you and forget your name afterwards, this is almost certainly the position he'd pick. But forget all that – we're assuming here that you're having sex with a guy who already knows your name, and the bottom line (ha ha) is, if you want excitement and stimulation, dogs appear to know more than you'd think, because it's a winner. He almost certainly isn't projecting other women's faces onto you, either, because he's too busy staring at your arse in a frenzy of lust.

So, now you've got your hang-ups out of the way, it's simply a matter of getting into position. A word first, though – if he only ever wants you in the doggy position, he may be a man with intimacy issues. Or a psychopath.

BOTTOMS UP!

It's not simply a matter of hands, knees and, well, bumps-a-daisy. If you merely get into the position you'd use to find a contact lens on a beige carpet, it's not quite enough. You need to present your bum, which:

a) makes the entrance easier to find
b) stimulates the front wall of your vagina
c) also drives him insane with desire.

Never forget that we share 98 per cent of our DNA with monkeys, and what do monkeys flash when they want to excite other monkeys? That's right, their bums. So, once on hands and knees, put your hands slightly in front of you; otherwise you'll crumple like a pack of cards when he thrusts, and then tilt your pelvis so your bum is sticking upwards. This also has the effect of making your waist look tiny – which is always good news. Part your legs, then he (kneeling behind you) can enter you from behind. He can reach your breasts which, because they're hanging down, are more sensitive, and he can also reach round and play with your clitoris. Or he can simply thrust away. This is a very intense position, because the angle of entry means he can touch the whole length of your vagina with his penis – so if he thrusts hard, expect to get carried away. If your arms start to ache, leave your bum sticking up, and lower yourself so your head's on the pillow – this also means he can kneel with your legs on either side of his lap, and makes for a less exhausting shag. You can even adapt it so you kneel on the bed, and he stands beside it – that gives an element of master–servant to the whole thing, and also means a very intense thrust, because he can put his whole weight behind it. Doggy-style can result in marvellous orgasms, but save it for when you're not feeling fragile – physically or emotionally.

sat on your lap

If you did want to have sex in a crowded nightclub, sitting on his lap would be the obvious way. Unless you were wearing hot pants, of course. It's a useful, go-anywhere position (buses, train toilets, planes, parties ...), but it's also good to use at home if you can't be bothered going upstairs to bed. Just make sure the chair you're sitting on isn't a rickety self-assembly flat-pack job, or you're likely to end your passionate encounter lying in a heap with a twisted ankle. Ideally, you need a sturdy kitchen chair – forget all that nonsense about rocking chairs, the fact that it's rocking makes absolutely no difference to sex – and just let him sit on it, with his pants round his ankles (or naked, if you prefer) while you sit elegantly on top with your skirt hitched up (or naked). You can face either way – but in the privacy of your own home it's much nicer to actually face him, so you can kiss him. Straddle him with a leg either side – if your feet don't touch the floor, make sure he's holding your bum, or has his hands tightly clasped around your waist – insert his willy, and off you go. You can't thrust, as the chair will wobble alarmingly, so just rock gently. Or, if you're an absolute sex goddess, and you're in a public place, use the vaginal muscles to squeeze and release his penis – further explanations of how to do this will appear later on, so don't worry. If you are in public, then sit side-saddle, and make small, grinding movements. Very small. Really – it's more obvious than you'd think. The lap position is also nice in bed, though – he sits or kneels on the bed, and you can face him for full-frontal body contact. If he sits with his legs in front of him, and you face him with yours on either side of him, it's a fantastically intimate position – and also allows for very deep penetration, which is, generally, a good thing.

spoons

This is the ideal lazyitis position, perfect for slightly hungover mornings, knackered nights, and any time when the idea of leaping about like a naked cheerleader fills you with exhaustion. It's so simple it's almost laughable – you lie side by side, facing the same way. He puts a leg over your hip, slips it in, and rocks gently, whilst playing with your breasts and clitoris by reaching round from behind. He can also kiss your neck adoringly. You, meanwhile, can reach his balls and stroke his bum by reaching behind you. And if that's all too impersonal, you can do it face to face, by lying on your other side, putting a leg over his hip, and getting it on the other way round. But then you have each other's morning breath and Edward Scissorhands hair to deal with. Still, nobody's perfect. Don't be tempted to try and lie with one leg underneath his, at the bottom of the leg-pile – it'll just go numb, and you'll be in agony after 30 seconds.

standing up

Standing-up sex is fantastic if you both happen to be 5'8". Or even 5'2", if you get off on midgets. But standing-up sex for people of different heights is like a jigsaw with half the pieces missing – it just doesn't fit together. Which is a shame, because vertical sex can be fantastic: not only is it rough-and-ready and passionate, it provides full access to each other's bodies. So it's definitely worth making the effort to get your bits at the right level. Of course, high heels help – but if you're not a high heels sort of girl (and, if not, why not?), the answer is simply to turn round, lean against the wall and stick your bum out so he can brace his arms against said wall, and enter you from behind. Forget those last-tango-in-Paris ideas you had about wrapping your legs round his waist while he thrusts manfully. He's more likely to keel forwards in a dumb show of pain and distress, as his lower back caves in to the pressure of having eight stone plus hanging off him like a giant barnacle. And, if you try to face him, you find it almost impossible to insert his penis – it's hard enough to insert a tampon in a standing position, let alone seven inches of leaping manhood. (Well, seven-ish.) If you do manage it, you'll need to keep one leg up around his waist – but it's a very rocky position. And, just because Kylie managed it in the *Kids* video, it doesn't mean you can, alright? They weren't actually having sex, after all.

other positions

You don't need any other positions. What you've got here will keep him and you happy for several years. And, when you get bored, just start again. 'Remember that thing we used to do before the children were born, darling?' 'Ooh, yes – right, I'll just lie back ...' However, you can utilize furniture apart from the bed. So ...

best furniture for having sex
(and best position to have it in ...)

1. Kitchen chair: He faces forward, you face him, climb on his lap and rock gently.
2. Kitchen table: He stands up, you lie back with your feet balanced on two kitchen chairs. Otherwise, you'll get table burns shunting back and forth.
3. Washing machine: You sit on the edge, pop it on spin cycle, and send him to tidy up while you have an orgasm. Alternately, lean over it while he takes you from behind.
4. Sofa: Just like bed really, but slightly narrower, him sitting up, you kneeling and facing him is best (unless the TV's really good).
5. In the shower: Standing up, again from behind, with your arms braced against the wall, but for God's sake make sure you use non-slip mats.

worst furniture for having sex

1. Coffee table: It'll break, and there's no position that won't give at least one of you carpet burns.

2. Armchair: Where, exactly, do you think you're going to fit? Unless you kneel down and he kneels behind you – but really, it's easier in bed.

3. At the sink: Because the sink is usually under a window. The window all your neighbours can see into. Come on, it's not late-night Channel 5, you know.

4. In the bath: Imagine trying to catch a goldfish in a washing-up bowl. Yes, that's you having sex in water. It's really not worth the bother.

5. In front of the fire: Despite what you may think, because the chances are, you'll get carried away, and one side of your body will end up bright red and covered in heat-induced thread veins. Nice.

Size doesn't matter
... or does it?

Condoms should be marketed in three sizes, jumbo, colossal and super-colossal so that men do not have to go in and ask for the small.

Barbara Seaman

Ever since he was a little boy with a willy the size of an acorn, your man has been secretly afraid that it won't measure up. For some reason – and it'd take a greater sexpert than I to figure out exactly why – men believe that a big penis is the ultimate badge of masculinity, kind of like having an Access All Areas tour laminate, driving a Formula One racing car, and scoring the winning goal for Inter Milan, all rolled into one. Maybe they believe that having a big penis means they'll produce more sperm, which means they'll impregnate more women, and therefore carry the family name down the generations. Or maybe they think all their power is tied up in their little extending telescope, like Samson's hair, so the bigger it is, the more likely they are to be a captain of industry with Bond Girls hanging off their arm every time they step outside the front door. Maybe they're just scared of getting teased by bigger boys in the school showers. The least likely reason, unfortunately, is that they desperately want to bring a woman pleasure, and figure having a big one is the best way to go about it. Although, for some, it may be a minor factor.

The truth is, however, that the best penis size for women is an average one – which is around 6–6.5 inches. Obviously, you won't be whisking out a tape measure the moment he drops his pants – but much bigger than that, you'll be able to tell because your eyes will automatically widen and your legs will slam shut as you envisage the manoeuvring necessary to get the thing any-where near you. Much smaller, however, and your well-trained eye will be able to cunningly assess the fact that it's probably going to get lost somewhere inside you, and be rattling around like a potholer in an underground cave, calling for help. But, even if you've just unpacked your new boyfriend to reveal a damp squib – or a Telecom Tower of terrifying proportions – don't scream in horror yet, because length isn't the only thing that mat-ters. Circumference is also important (for those who were day-dreaming about boys during maths lessons, that would be the width). And, even if it looks as if it's been designed by a spatially challenged committee, there's still stuff you can do to make it work during sex. So he shouldn't panic – and neither should you.

when it's too big

In a sense, there's no such thing as 'too big'. Then again, in a sense, Chris Evans is quite a shy bloke. For our purposes, 'too big' basically means, wide enough to need help entering your bits, like getting a fat guy through an airport security check. Or, more plainly, if your put your hand round it, your fingers don't quite meet. It may also look scarily long – but this is actually less trou-blesome to deal with, because there's no law that says he has to push it right in, till it's bashing away at the entrance to your cervix like an insensitive bailiff. All he needs to do is insert it three-quarters of the way in – because, amazingly enough, your vagina only has nerve-endings in the first three inches. Which doesn't necessarily mean that a thimble-sized penis will do the business – but it does mean that 10 throbbing inches is not necessarily your passport to sexual ecstasy. Unless it's battery-operated and made of plastic, obviously.

GETTING READY

The big key to having a good time with a large willy is simply lubrication. And, believe me, if I could think of a more attractive word for it, I would – any suggestions on a postcard, please. If your own natural resources aren't quite flowing enough – and they should be, if he gets the foreplay thing right first – then it's back to our old pal KY jelly and its like. Rubbing a squeeze round the entrance and a bit over his penis should make the two fit together like a well-oiled lock and key – but, if not, you may be subconsciously tensing your muscles in fright, and he'll need to keep stroking around there to help you relax. He can even use a finger or thumb to lightly stretch the entrance – that's 'lightly' though, remember, as you don't want to feel like you're about to give birth in a Crimean field hospital.

The only real worry is, once he is inside you and thrusting away, he's going to want to put it all in – which, when inserted fast, is possibly going to be painful. So you need to know which positions are best for Mr Big Willy (and you can call him that too – but only if you want his ego to expand like a hot-air balloon. Possibly not, then.)

BIG POSITIONS

The easiest way to accommodate a big willy is you on top. It's a perfect position for controlling the action, because he can't thrust too hard without your say-so – unless, of course, he's a body-builder with hips like pistons. Also, be aware that you don't have to slide up and down his willy like a pole-dancer on elastic – if you just insert it a few inches – just the first 14 or so, ho, ho ... then you can grind your hips round in a circle, and experience the feeling of fullness and stimulation that women are actually referring to when they praise big willies, without feeling like a speared tuna.

Another winning position is legs wide apart – it's not like he'll complain ... obviously, this is your best bit for getting your bits as wide as they'll go – but don't put a cushion under your bum this time, as the deeper angle of penetration will hurt. Just bend your knees slightly, and use them to grip his hips and, thus, control the pace of the thrusting. Simple.

ADVANTAGES OF A BIG WILLY

1. You are going out with an exceptionally confident man. So he will not have any need to purchase expensive penis substitutes such as Ferraris, Harley Davidsons and Lear jets. Which means he won't spend every weekend tinkering with the engine when he could be shagging.
2. It fills you up, and therefore has the potential to stimulate all possible nerve-endings, which may, ultimately, result in fantastic orgasm. Can't complain, then.
3. If you get off on eyeing up men's crotches, you've got something to look at when you're bored.

DISADVANTAGES OF A BIG WILLY

1. It might be painful.
2. He may think he's God's gift, and therefore be less committed than he should be to fidelity. After all, there's plenty to go round, girls ...
3. You need lots of foreplay before it'll go in easily – so it's not ideal for quickies.

when it's little

Be aware your guy has probably grown up humiliated by his diminutive dimensions. He's met you after a lifetime of crouching in the shower, wondering about vacuum-pumps, and vainly telling himself it looks bigger from the front. So you have to be very, very careful how you approach this. That is, unlike the confident Big Willy man, you can't say, 'Christ, it's a bit small. Why don't we try this position ...?' So you're simply going to have to manoeuvre him secretly into the right place. The good news is, if it's short but wide, you have no problem – it's more likely to drive you wild than the long thin kind, because of the pressure it exerts on the hypersenstive vaginal opening. If it's both short and thin, however, his little flower of manhood can still excite you – it really isn't a reason to finish a relationship. Not unless he likes Phil Collins as well.

You just have to know how to be creative with what you have got. After all, anything over 2.5 inches is considered 'normal' by the medical profession (below that, it's called a micropenis, and if that's your boy he almost certainly doesn't want to discuss it), so you've got plenty to work with.

You still need lubrication to get anything inside you – but obviously, perhaps, not the giant quantities you need for Mr Big Willy. As we've established, size is not that important – but it matters that you can feel him in there, to avoid humiliating 'Is that it?' style moments. There are two things that you can do, then, that are particularly useful.

TWO USEFUL THINGS
Tighten your muscles

Tightening your own vaginal muscles seems kind of like saying, 'He hasn't got any money, so I can't buy shoes'. That is, why's it your responsibility? Well, simply because you'll both have a better time if you do. Nobody's suggesting that your muscle tone is anything other than perky – however, unless you're a Thai bargirl who can fire ping-pong balls across the room with her inner muscles, you can always improve it. And, to do that, you need to do Kegel exercises (named because they were devised by Dr Kegel – possibly a close friend of Dr Graftenberg, who popped up in the last chapter. Maybe they just hung out together, chatting about ladies' bits.) The good news is, they're a lot simpler than the normal kind of exercise misery necessary to improve muscle tone. All you do is locate the muscles you'd use to stop a wee halfway through – say, if Johnny Depp was at the door, and you knew that if you didn't get off the toilet sharpish, he'd be gone forever. These are the pelvic floor muscles, and all you have do to tighten them is squeeze and release. If it helps, you can mutter 'Johnny!' to yourself with every squeeze. The good news is, you can do them anywhere, because, being internal, it's a lot simpler than the usual sweaty frenzy that muscle toning involves. And no one can see you doing them – unless you do happen to work in a Bangkok bar, in which case you certainly don't need my advice.

All you do is clench and release, as many repetitions as you like. And the end result (after a couple of weeks, if you remember to do a batch every day) will be that when he puts his penis inside you, your muscles will grip more effectively than a sailor 20 feet up a ship's mast – and therefore your nerve-endings will be so much more stimulated. So will his, but hey – you're doing him a favour, so let's not worry about that.

Make his willy bigger

Forget those Handy Pumps offered in the back of questionable magazines (if, indeed, you even knew about them). What you're aiming to do is make his willy expand to be the biggest it can be. And, believe me, it can build itself up with the right kind of stimulation. Obviously, you know that an erection is created from spongy chambers that fill with blood when he gets excited. You really didn't think it was little bones, forming a mini Eiffel Tower then obediently collapsing again, did you? Did you ...?

So it figures that the more blood there is pumping round, the harder and, consequently, the bigger he gets. Which is where you come in. Of course, he's going to have a fairly decent erection simply at the sight of your naked body. But it can be improved. If you want it to swell to epic proportions – particularly at the tip – a few licks are your best bet. Just hold the shaft, caress the top with your tongue, and generally act as though any minute you might embark on a full-scale blowjob. He'll be so giddy with anticipation, it will rise to its fullest extent in moments. Alternatively, use your hand, but stop before he orgasms, naturally. At which point, in he goes – bigger than ever before.

If he really has got a tiny one, and you've tried the above, and still feel like he's merely a moped rider in the Blackwall Tunnel, you can still enjoy screaming orgasms (no, no, not with his best friend ...). It's simply a matter of working with what you have, as your mother used to tell you when you moaned about your flat chest.

HANDY TECHNIQUES

Place the tip of his penis so it's resting on your clitoris, with the shaft just inside your labia (how I hate that little word). Here's where lubrication is helpful – because he's going to move up and down, rubbing against you, and stimulating every part of your bits, whilst at the same time feeling strange and delightful sensations himself. Who cares if it's the size of a thimble, frankly? You can't lose.

Shut your legs, woman ...

The smaller it is, the more friction you'll want to create, so the best position for this is when he lies on top of you (always a winner) with his thighs parted, while you keep yours together. When he puts his penis inside you, the reduced space caused by your clamped legs will make the fit much tighter – and therefore he'll be easier to feel as he thrusts away. The only problem might be resisting the temptation to part your legs, at which point the sensation will fade somewhat. Another handy trick is to use a ribbed condom. Some sexperts suggest you can use a few, to pad him out – but how the hell's that going to make him feel, being bundled up like a six-year-old about to play in the snow? Just one will suffice.

Other good positions include any which maximize the depth and angle of penetration. And the ideal position is the stuffed turkey – he kneels up, you put your ankles on his shoulders – or, if you're feeling agile, pull your knees up to your chest. That way, he can see exactly what he's doing, which offers visual stimulation and minimizes the chances of him falling out, and your vagina's at an angle which offers plenty of G-spot stimulation.

Also, doing it from behind works well with a small one – you get deep penetration, coupled with the chance for him to reach round and stroke your clitoris. Again, if he's short but wide, this is the ideal position, as every nerve at the entrance to your vagina will feel the pressure. If he's not, it's still pretty good.

PSYCHOLOGICAL CUNNING

It bears repeating that you must never, ever, use the word 'small' in conjunction with his penis. It's like him using 'fat' and 'your stomach' in the same sentence – only worse, because if you did have a fat stomach and hated it, you could always lose weight by not eating cakes for a while. But if he's got a small penis, he knows very well that there's not a thing he can do about it. Don't be fooled if he says, 'Look, I know it's smaller than average' and agree with him. Simply say 'It looks more than enough to me'. He won't know if the last guy you went to bed with had a penis like a redwood tree, and he certainly won't thank you for telling him.

SMALL GOOD POINTS

1. There's no way you're going to gag when you give him a blowjob. In fact, blowjobs are more fun altogether, as there's more space for your tongue to try exciting new tricks.
2. He'll be insecure, and therefore less likely to run off with another woman, for fear that she'll laugh and point. He knows that you are a goddess because you don't even seem to think it's small. Or, if you do, you sure keep quiet.
3. He won't give you cystitis by bashing away with his mighty truncheon. And, more importantly, he'll probably have a Ferrari.

SMALL BAD POINTS

1. You might not get as much stimulation.
2. He's probably insecure, and therefore you'll have to spend hours counselling him about how desirable he is.
3. You can't say anything even slightly negative, however frustrating things may be.

a quick guide to the penis

Whether it's big or small, it helps to know exactly what goes where when it comes to the miracle of engineering that is your boy's equipment. So, if you thought it was just a sticky-up thing that goes up and down, read on. You might learn something.

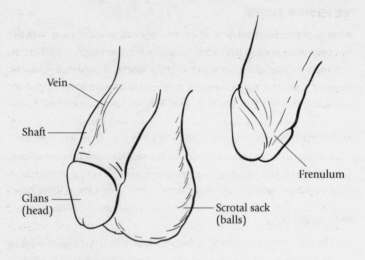

Vein

Shaft

Glans
(head)

Frenulum

Scrotal sack
(balls)

THE FORESKIN

The rather unattractive phrase 'cut or uncut' does not refer to operations for transsexuals, but to circumcision. So, if he has no foreskin that pulls up over the head of his penis (like the boy with the green jumper in The Bash Street Kids), he's probably circumcized. If he's Jewish, it's entirely likely that he is – and other men may have been snipped because of infection, or a tight foreskin. It's supposed to be cleaner and more hygienic – the bonus is, it also makes the head extra-sensitive as it has no protective covering. But it makes it slightly more confusing to give handjobs – you need to use lubrication, and then just pull your hand up and down over the head as you normally would. Try and get a smooth rhythm going, despite the lack of movable foreskin.

If he has a foreskin, it's vital that he washes underneath it daily, as all sort of murky things can lurk under there – and you really don't want them inside you. Interestingly, if you hold the foreskin back during sex (known as 'Florentine' sex), it speeds up ejaculation. Well I never.

THE HEAD

This is the bulb-like bit at the top – note the tiny hole where the sperm comes out – and also urine, but hopefully you won't be having much to do with that aspect of the willy's technical workings. It's very sensitive, and responds well to licking, and light stroking. Never squeeze, however. It's not a desk toy, you know.

FRENULUM

Now we're getting technical. This is the piece of skin on the underside (i.e. the side facing you when it's erect) that joins the head and the shaft. It's extremely sensitive, to the extent that some men don't even like it being touched. Some, however, adore it. It's best if you simply run your tongue gently around it, flickering it back and forth – using your fingers directly on it runs the risk of pulling it. And you thought you were jumpy about your bits.

SHAFT

The main section, and the bit you grasp when you're giving him a handjob. It can take slightly rougher treatment than the rest, but never yank it outwards; only up and down. The vein that runs up the front of the erection is more sensitive – don't press on it either, because you'll effectively create a tourniquet, and stop the blood-flow – not ideal, under the circumstances.

If his willy was an ice cream, the shaft would be the cone. And sex would be very chilly. Any over-enthusiastic grabbing and squeezing will have him deflating faster than a popped dinghy. But on the other hand, it's not wise to be too delicate about it, either – most men don't want the shaft of their willy, which is pulsating with sexual longing, to be handled like a wilting carnation, either.

THE BALLS

Often neglected, the balls are where all the vital sperm production gets sorted out, so it seems grossly unfair to ignore them. Testicles are erogenous zones in their own right, and respond exceptionally well to caresses. If you can get one – or, remarkably, both – in your mouth, it will give him a lovely feeling of comfort and warmth, like a 1950s Christmas film, coupled with a strange tingling of lust. Otherwise, he'll still appreciate you fondling them, and kissing and nibbling – no teeth, mind – on the skin. If you want to venture further afield, locate his perineum – the bit between his balls and his arse – and press gently. This has a marvellous effect on his prostate gland, and will magically intensify all sensations felt by the penis. But, once again, don't forget that 'gentle but firm' is not the same as 'agonizingly hard'. Unless you get off on playing Nursie, that is. Simple stroking of the whole general area is satisfactory, particularly when coupled with penis fondling. But a word of advice – never, ever, squeeze his balls for 'fun'. Unless you can't think how else to finish with him.

things never to say about his penis

1. Is it in yet? God, sorry. I couldn't feel a thing.
2. How cute: it looks just like a penis, only smaller.
3. No, but when it's erect it'll be fine ... It is?
4. Look, I just don't think it's going to reach my G spot. Do you mind if I use the vibrator instead?
5. Could you just nip and wash? It smells a bit off.
7. God! But it's nothing like my ex's ... I mean, not in a bad way, it's just ... not what I expected.
8. Is it supposed to bend like that?
9. That reminds me, I must renew my National Trust membership. (Acorns, see?)
10. Oh. Best not bother, eh?

orgasm

In the case of some women, orgasms take a bit of time.
Before signing on with a partner, make sure you are willing to
lay aside, say, the month of June, with sandwiches having to
be brought in.

Bruce Jay Friedman

If there's one thing guaranteed to cause sexual problems, it's the whole notion of orgasm. It seems so
simple – you both have bits; put the bits together,
fiddle around, and bang! Suddenly it's a firework display, crashing waves and exploding champagne corks, all over the bed. It
only it were that simple – but there's barely a woman in the
world who hasn't at some point suffered some insecurity relating
to her orgasm or lack of it. And, given that while men have some
orgasm-related problems too (like 'can't fit 15 into a working
day' … nope, just kidding), women tend to have more difficulty
coming at will, we'll examine the woman-and-orgasms situation
first.

what is an orgasm?

You'd be amazed at the number of women who aren't actually sure what an orgasm is. Is it that feeling of relaxation after sex? Or possibly that sort of itchy tingling down there? Or just a slight feeling like a sneeze? Well, actually, no it's not. Technically, an orgasm happens when you're so sexually stimulated that your genitalia fill with blood, and all your nerve-endings are crying out for release – every muscle in your body then tenses up, and, if the stimulation continues, it'll suddenly be released. Your vagina contracts five or six times, your breasts swell up to a third of their size again (which is good news for Wonderbra girls) and, though it's impossible to describe, it's generally a total-body-tingling experience which feels very nice indeed. Of course, everyone experiences it differently – to some women, it's like sitting at the front of a rollercoaster; to others, like a gramme of top-grade Colombian snorted whilst sitting on Brad Pitt's knee; and to still others, it's merely a pleasant way to cure insomnia.

Although a few lucky girls claim to be able to orgasm merely from having their nipples stroked – or, in a few truly weird cases, their big toe/elbow/nose licked – orgasms are generally considered to be genital-based. And, while vast amounts of time have been wasted debating the relative merits of a vaginal and clitoral orgasm, current thinking suggests that they amount to the same thing. The bottom line is, you have a massive concentration of nerve-endings down there – the clitoris, is, in fact, simply a miniature version of a penis – and so therefore, with enough of the right kind of stimulation, you're going to come sooner or later. In theory, at any rate. In truth, it can take many women hours to come – particularly if you aren't 100 per cent relaxed. He can be alternating between his hand, his tongue, a giant vibrator and a rotating banana for two hours with no luck whatsoever if you aren't in the mood. Because, while most men can come regardless of whether they've had the day from hell and are suffering chronic exhaustion, women have to be mentally ready before they can be physically ready. It's like there's a hotline between our brains and our bits: 'She's worried about tomorrow's presentation – order emergency shutdown now!' Whereas with men, the link-up tends to be bits-brain, rather than the other way round – 'Look, I know you're tired, but she's wearing stockings! Come on, make the effort ...' Which is, quite possibly, one reason why orgasming isn't quite so easy for you.

how to have one – rub your bits

If that doesn't work, we may have to get a bit more technical. Having established that you're only likely to orgasm satisfactorily if you're mentally relaxed and turned on, there are various paths you can take. All of them involve stimulating your clitoris, the most important key here being 'If it ain't broke, don't fix it'. That is, if he's manipulating it in a way that's starting to feel great, for God's sake don't let him suddenly flex his wrist and change position and pressure 'to vary things'. Unless you're already massively excited, this will just send you straight back to square one.

The first thing you – and he – needs is patience. Because, if you've not been to bed together enough times to have worked out what's required, it's probably going to take a while. Some women take 10 minutes to orgasm with constant stimulation – some can take an hour or more. So, if he's tutting and checking his watch every five minutes, you're hardly going to be sinking gently into a web of wondrous sensation. More likely worrying about whether you're missing *ER*, and how long his patience is actually going to hold. There's nothing more likely to kill an orgasm stone dead than trying to hurry it up. Think of it as a shy woodland creature: you can't stuff a hand in its burrow and wrench it out; you've got to coax and cajole it, with gentle stroking and soft words, and make it feel reassured enough to emerge into the sunlight.

BEGINNER'S TIPS

First, you need to be wet enough, to put in bluntly. Stroking your clitoris when it's dry will simply make it sore and overwrought. So, if you aren't already crazed with lust at the sight of your man's

Homer Simpson boxer shorts, again, bring on the lubricating gel. Niiice. Then, all he has to do – initially, at least – is rub his finger in small, gentle circles across and around your clitoris. It's likely that direct pressure will be too much – but a lot of men assume that the only way to get you to come is to be violently eager, and rub away like a window-cleaner. This will not work, your clitoris will merely retreat, defeated and unnerved. Tell him to do it as if he's polishing a very fragile piece of antique jewellery to a shine. Once you get more worked up – and he'll be able to tell by your general pants, gasps and writhings – he can afford to intensify the pressure very slightly, either by adding another finger, to stimulate a further area of your labia, or sliding a finger into your vagina. But if he does anything you aren't keen on, or find distracting, far better to let him know now than lie there mentally groaning with frustration – either just move his hand to where you want it and say, 'That feels amazing' or murmur, 'Oh that felt so great – it's all nice, but could you go back to what you were doing?' Don't make him feel he's made a hideous error of judgement simply by attempting to stop the cramp in his fingers – but don't pretend you're having a great time when you're not, either, because it wastes both your time.

Of course, as you progress, you can try all manner of different touches. But, for a sure-fire orgasm, the easiest way is clitoral stroking, coupled with nipple stimulation. He can lick or twiddle – just so long as he doesn't chew, or suck and blow like a faulty vacuum cleaner spewing out dust.

A MORE ADVANCED TECHNIQUE

The majority of women don't come through vaginal stimulation alone – the figure who do is estimated at about 25 per cent or less. So any nonsense from your boyfriend regarding 'why it isn't working' should be given short shrift. Most women experience very positive feelings from sex itself – but, unless his penis is perfectly designed to stimulate your G spot, which happens to be configured to leap into orgasm at the slightest touch, it's likely you're not going to come during intercourse unless he's stimulating your clit at the same time – either through a position such as the CAT, or with his fingers, or by holding a vibrator against you. Or, of course, if he's a Russian acrobat, with his tongue. Whichever you use, it's still likely to take a while. Women who double up in orgasmic delight at the first touch of a penis are only ever found in the kind of porn magazines that 15-year-old boys base their knowledge of sex on. And really, your guy should have moved on from that place by now.

DURING SEX

It can be a little like rubbing your tummy and patting your head to attempt to get the right level of stimulation for your clitoris at the same time as he's thrusting in and out. Obviously, missionary position is right out – you're more likely to have each other's eyes out than an orgasm, and there'll be elbows flying everywhere. You on top, however, can work – but it works best if he's simply holding his finger (or his thumb, which works brilliantly in this position) against your clitoris, so you can rock against it. If he tries to move as well, your rhythm will go completely to pot – trust me.

Another excellent position is a variation on the scissors position – you lie side by side, put one of your legs alongside his and the other on top, insert his penis, and he reaches down and rubs your clitoris at the same time.

WITH HELP

There is a simple answer to the whole 'can't move fingers in rhythm with willy' dilemma – which is a vibrator. All you have to do it flick the switch, and hold it alongside your clitoris – he can rub it up and down, or in circles, or simply keep it still while you move and he thrusts. It saves on aching digits, and is ultimately more likely to result in an intercourse orgasm than any amount of manual fiddling about. Only don't choose one that's too big – you don't want him to suddenly start comparing and contrasting halfway through, as he looks at his little runner bean, gamely thrusting away next to your 12 inch King of Love model.

MULTIPLE

There is no consensus as to what exactly constitutes a multiple orgasm. Is it when you have more than one orgasm during a sex session? Is it when you have one, really lengthy, orgasm, that keeps rippling away long after the appointed time for ending? Is it, in fact, a myth, created by the peddlers of exactly the porn mags that make men grow up imagining that all women are in a constant state of giddy arousal? No one can say. But, if you can have more than one orgasm in a session, it really isn't important what you call it – it's just a handy trick to master. One way to pursue Orgasm Meltdown is the stop–start technique, beloved of Californian sex gurus. But I'm from Manchester, and it works just as well here.

It relies on a bit of self-control from both of you. But mainly you. It might help – and it'd certainly perk things up – if you get your bloke to tie you up first. Then, while he kisses you, caresses your breasts and generally pays close attention to your erogenous zones, he rubs your clitoris right to the point of orgasm. At the point when you shriek, 'Oh my God, don't stop!' he stops, and returns to nibbling your nipples and licking your neck for a few moments. Then he starts caressing again, this time slipping a finger inside you as well, until again you indicate that you're about to take off. And stops. Done three or four times, this will ideally raise you to a state of panting orgasmic excitement. After the third time, you won't know if you're coming continuously or not, and by the fourth time you definitely will be. The trick is to make sure he stops at just the right moment to leave you hovering on the edge.

The only drawback with the pursuit of multiple orgasm, in whatever form it takes, is that, after you've come once, your bits can feel highly sensitized and will probably need a rest. You certainly won't want any more manual action for a while. What you need is relief from the sensitivity, from his tongue. So once you've come, if he gets right back down there straight away, he needs to lick you around the area, not directly on it – just gentle caresses with his whole tongue – and then he can get more specific as your clitoris stops gasping with exhaustion, and move a bit closer to it. As he circles your most sensitive bits with his mouth – much gentler than a finger – to your surprise, the orgasmic feelings will return faster than you thought possible.

SIMULTANEOUS ORGASM

Coming at the same time is one of those things that can happen occasionally, and isn't technically impossible – but it's kind of like it snowing at Christmas. It'd be nice and everything, but you know the chances are that it won't happen. Really, it's a little overrated anyway – it's always nice to watch your partner come, because then you get that little feeling of 'I did that!' triumph, and it's quite a turn-on as well. If you're both busy riding your own personal express trains to Pleasure Central, you hardly notice each other's there. Forget all that tantric oneness business, unless your name's Sting – for the ordinary mortal, it's not always worth the bother.

But, if you really are determined, the best chance of arriving together is to monitor progress throughout. So you have to tell each other how near you think you are to coming – because otherwise how are you going to know? He should take his cue from you – because, generally speaking, he's got a little more control over his orgasm, as he can simply thrust extra-fast and inevitably come within seconds. When it starts building up, let him know – and this is where a vibrator comes in handy, because you really don't want the speed or the pressure to change at this point – and whisper to him when he should go for it.

With luck, seeing each other so worked up should push you both over the edge at around the same time – like climbers roped together. But if not, it's cool, as he can just watch you come after him. It's not like you're losing out, is it?

NOISE

Possibly the most fraught aspect of orgasm is how much noise is normal. Some girls are *When Harry Met Sally* shriekers, some make less noise than a mouse with a furball stuck in its throat.

Either is fine. But if you're the first kind, you may be embarrassed at your compulsion to yell 'Oh! My! God!' at top volume, or scream and shout when you come. Well, don't fret on his account. The vast majority of men love to think that they've caused a woman to feel so abandoned – he's highly unlikely to be lying there thinking, 'In the name of God, can't she shut up for five minutes?' More likely, 'Christ, am I responsible for that? What a love god I must be.'

The truth is, if you are a screamer, there's not a whole lot you can do about it – and it's better out than in, because if you start worrying about it you'll never relax enough to enjoy an orgasm anyway. The only downside is your neighbours. If your bedroom's next to theirs, it may be best to hide under the covers when you come. Otherwise, they'll only be jealous.

If you're the mouse kind of girl, that's fine as well. It doesn't matter what your boyfriend says about 'Are you enjoying yourself?' or 'You seem very quiet' or 'Am I doing it right?' If carrying on like an opera diva on the closing night of La Scala isn't your bag, he's going to have to put up with it. Simply remember to reassure him every so often that you really are having a good time – a little intake of breath here, a sigh of excitement there. Otherwise, he's going to think you're mentally sorting your sock drawer, while he rummages about uselessly in your pants. Unless that's the situation, in which case, better have a serious talk.

FAKING

There is never an excuse for faking an orgasm. Forget all that crap about 'It can be justified if it's to save his feelings' or 'Well, if you're really tired ...' No, it can't. All it does is put barriers between you. Basically, faking an orgasm is lying to him at what should be a deeply intimate moment between you. It's also pointless – you're left unsatisfied, and he assumes he's doing the right thing when he isn't. If your relationship isn't solid enough for you to be able to say, 'Look, I'm having a great time, but I really don't think I'm going to come tonight – my body's gone on strike' or some such, then you shouldn't even be in bed with him.

And, if you have faked up to now, whilst admitting it isn't a particularly pleasant option, don't be sucked into the trap of feeling you have to carry on faking. You're a bright girl, there are ways round it. Say, 'I know I always come this way, but let's try it a different way – I heard it could be even better.' Hell, make up a quote from me if you like. Anything – just stop pretending, because it's doing you both a disservice.

his orgasm

Your man's orgasm is somewhat simpler to achieve than yours, possibly because to procreate the species he absolutely has to come. For you, it's like getting a bonus track on a CD – it's always nice, but not strictly necessary. But, unless he's 16, and therefore orgasmic at the sight of a nice pair of legs, a hint of cleavage or, indeed, anything in a skirt, including Lily Savage, he does need a bit of input in order to come.

HOW TO MAKE A MAN COME

Rub his willy, simple as that. The ultimate aim is the ejaculation of roughly 500,000,000 sperm as far as they'll go (up to two feet on a good day, or straight into the end of the condom, depending). And it's simple friction which causes it to start its perilous journey into the outside world. So, it figures, the harder you rub, or he thrusts, the closer he gets to orgasm. It isn't generally the case that you're going to have trouble – if you aren't handling it right, most men will tell you exactly what to do, rather than simply lie there, thinking, 'I hope she stops soon so I can go to sleep'. But there are certain other problems you may, er, come across.

PREMATURE EJACULATION

Almost every man in the world has suffered this at some stage. And all are united in finding it deeply embarrassing, shameful, and a badge of dishonour awarded by the State of Manhood. You, meanwhile, are probably just vaguely flattered that he's so red-hot for you. But if it happens regularly, don't click your tongue and hiss, 'For Christ's sake, what are you, 13? Could you just try and hold it together for five seconds?' because that may well mean he never gets an erection again. There are certain techniques, however, that you can try, which are likely to prolong the excitement for his hair-trigger willy and, therefore, give you a little longer to enjoy it, too. The cause is usually either over-excitement or nerves – both of which tend to happen at first, and disappear when you've been together a while. But if it doesn't:

Squeezing

A useful technique is the squeeze, which can be performed shortly before the point of no return, and has the magical effect of instantly calming things down. Just grasp his penis firmly, and press your fingers on the rim, just below the head. If he's inside you, you can equally squeeze at the base. This should have the effect of halting the blood-flow briefly, and slowing things down.

Stop–start

A particularly fine trick, involving, as it does, maximum pleasure for you. Allow him to get within half a minute or so of orgasm – then stop for another 30 seconds. Of course, this works best if you're either giving him a handjob, or on top – otherwise, he's likely to mutter, 'Stop? Yeah, right,' and carry straight on. Assuming he's agreeing to this technique, then, continue stopping and starting, each time letting him get a little more worked up, until you've had your fun – at which point, he'll experience a madly explosive orgasm, due to the lengthy build-up.

Masturbate first

If neither of these tips appear to be working, there is one option left – get him to masturbate to orgasm (or do it for him) half an hour before intercourse. Depending on his age, he should be able to get another erection within that time and, having come once, theoretically, he'll last longer when you have sex. Unless, of course, he simply finds that he's desperately oversensitized, and leaps into orgasmic action seconds later. Hey, but at least you tried.

If it's a real problem and, months on, it's not improved, it's almost certainly anxiety-related. Either stop saying, 'Let's see how you do tonight, Trigger' and cackling, or, if you're a nice person, suggest that a little psychosexual counselling may not go amiss.

IMPOTENCE

Nearly all men will occasionally suffer from impotence – usually due to stress, nerves, exhaustion or illness. But, if it becomes an ongoing problem, he needs to see his GP (or, if the GP is a crusty old family friend, his GUM clinic) to discover whether the cause is psychological or physical. If you're supportive, you'll go along with him – it's a highly difficult thing for a man to confront, and he'll need support. And you ordering a crate of Viagra and taking the phone off the hook won't necessarily solve the underlying problem. Sounds quite fun, though, admittedly.

things to say at orgasm

1. It's so big!
2. Oh, God! Oh, my God!
3. Oh, yes, [insert his name here]!
4. I love you! (Unless it's a first date, in which case you'll be finishing your orgasm alone.)
5. Don't stop! Oh! Oh!

things not to say at orgasm

1. Hurt me!
2. Oh, Daddy/Mummy!
3. Oh, [insert ex-boyfriend's name]!
4. No, stop! Stop! (He'll be very confused.)
5. Oh, I hate you! You bastard! (To you, it's passion; to him, merely character assassination.)

CHAPTER NINE

Sex toys

There are a number of mechanical devices which increase sexual arousal, particularly in women. Chief among these is the Mercedes-Benz 380SL convertible.

P. J. O'Rourke

Sometimes, the full range of body parts is simply not enough for the kind of sexual fun you want. For a more adventurous thrill, you need sex toys – whose usefulness is proved by the fact that, throughout time, couples have used inanimate objects to boost their sexual pleasure, from wooden dildos to embroidery silk with knots tied in it. (Yes, all will be explained, don't fret.)

However, whilst in the old days they used to be known as 'marital aids' and were aimed at dysfunctional couples whose only hope of orgasm was a flesh-pink vibrator that looked like a surgical appliance, nowadays there are swish boutiques selling every variety of Adult Toy, with absolutely no Erectile Dysfunction graphs in sight. However, the problem is that, while sex shops like Ann Summers and Sh! may stock every conceivable kind of buzzing willy-substitute, you don't know which kind is going to drive you insane with ecstasy, and which is simply going to leave you with a flat battery and sore bits. And you can't order everything you fancy from the catalogue and send back the ones that don't work, either. (Look, you just can't, OK? It isn't hygienic.) Plus there is the fact that shopping for sex toys, whilst entirely out of the closet, and happily practised by nuns, vicars and bishops – well, probably – is still verging on thoroughly embarrassing. Then again, every girl should have a box of tricks – just don't pack it when you go abroad. You really don't want your Giant Loverman vibrator and fluffy handcuffs popping up on the X-ray machine, to the guffawing amusement of several bored customs officials.

why sex toys?

Why not? Forget all that purist nonsense about how sex should be enough with just your bodies in perfect harmony – it is, but sometimes you don't just want a glass of wine, you want a cocktail with an umbrella and a maraschino cherry on top. At least, you do if you're as tacky as me – and sex toys are the multi-coloured tequila sunrises of sex. They liven things up, they add a new dimension to your sexual shenanigans, and they're unbelievably handy if you're going through a manless patch. You just have to be careful not to get too attached to the things, or your new boyfriend may be a little put out when he wakes from a deep sleep to find you locked in a passionate clinch with several inches of humming silicone. Vibrators are excellent for encouraging an orgasm when his fingers are getting weary and, if you favour the sensation of two penises caressing your bits, they save all the emotional trouble of involving another man, not to mention cutting out any ejaculation/impotence/personality problems. There's no need for your bloke to get all insecure either, because they can feel just as good to him as they do to you. In fact, there are only two unbreakable rules when it comes to sex toys.

1. Keep them clean.
2. Always remember to hide them when your mother comes to stay.

what you can get

It's impossible to round up every device on the market – if we did, we'd be waist-deep in jiggling silicone and gyrating plastic (which sounds fine, except not much work would get done), but there are certain basic types of sex toy, on which all the others are simply a variation of some sort. Depending on your erotic requirements, you may simply want a small, efficient vibrator to keep in the bedside drawer – or you may wish to stock a trunk with all manner of esoteric props, to be whisked out whenever things need spicing up. Either way, let's start with the basics.

VIBRATORS

Vibrators come in far more colours, shapes and sizes than penises. It's a good job men are generally secure, or they'd be led to believe that what we really want is a 12-inch blue jelly dildo with a giant blackberry moulded on top. In fact, perhaps we do. In the last few years, the range available has expanded dramatically, though the bestseller remains the Rampant Rabbit, a large vibrator with a rotating tip containing little balls, and a clitoral-stimulator attachment. But if your taste doesn't stretch to such a definite statement of intent, there are plenty more discreet versions to, er, tickle your fancy.

Battery

Plastic, battery-operated vibrators tend to be relatively small – around 7–10 inches. These are the 'handbag toys' of the vibrating world, i.e. they do what they say on the packet, with no messing about, and no fancy-pants attachments. Usually limited to two speeds (slow and fast). They're ideal when you want a quick orgasm, without wishing for the entire sex-simulation experience. The pros are: they're smallish, discreet and quiet. The cons are:

they feel like the plastic they are, they're very hard and, while they work well for a quick clitoral session, they're rather unappealing to put inside you. Plus, of course, you risk the dismal misery of the battery running out just as you're about to come.

Electronic

These are the deluxe PlayStation of vibrators, with more power and longevity than their battery-operated cousins. Usually larger (up to 14 inches – argh) with multi-speed dials, and various clitoris, G-spot and anus-tickling devices that can be attached, they're vibrators for the serious thrill-seeker. They are, however, probably best used alone, because the fact is, you are going to look a tad silly with a massive humming dildo attached to a wire leaping all over the bed. Some women, though, need a lot of heavy stimulation before they can come, and these vibrators provide it – it's kind of like sitting on a spin-cycle washing machine, in an express train, at the epicentre of an earthquake. Fairly serious stuff, then.

Silicone

This substance is slightly jelly-like, and therefore picks up body heat much faster than plastic, so feels much more 'real' – particularly if you want to shut your eyes and pretend that it's not a seven-inch pole, it's actually Brad Pitt, and he wants you now. It's also much more flexible than plastic, and works better if you want to insert it inside you and set it to vibrate against your G-spot, because it feels almost like a penis. I only said almost. This type come in all manner of colours, and for those girls who don't crave a penis-substitute (maybe you're going through a 'militant lesbian' phase, or some such) you can rest assured that a blue, sparkly wand with a miniature goddess moulded on the top – these exist, I've seen them – will look nothing like a penis. But it will give you an exceptionally good time when switched on and placed against your clitoris. Only you can know which kind suits you – the rotating tip? the foreskin-alike sheath? the clitoris-caressing bobbly bit? But you really can't go wrong with about eight inches of silicone, as long as it has adjustable speeds. Just try to keep in mind that men may be useful for some things. A vibrator is not going to kill a spider in the bath, is it? Then again, if it's 12 inches of solid power, it may well scare it to death.

THE BUTTERFLY

These are aimed entirely at women, and consist of a couple of elastic loops, and a small buzzing disc. You wear it under your knickers like a thong, place the disc against your clitoris, and voilà, instant orgasm wherever you happen to be. You can also get them with remote-control devices, so your boyfriend can press a button and have you screeching with joy on the other side of the pub. Do be careful where you wear it, though – you really don't want an orgasm in the middle of your job interview. Unless you're auditioning for *When Harry Met Sally II*, of course.

DILDOS

Dildos are simply penis-shaped items that don't vibrate. They're useful if you long for that filled-up feeling or, again, if you fancy something up your bum as well while he's inside your vagina. Or indeed, up his. Most people use switched-off vibrators, but you can buy specially made dildos, in plastic, silicone or rubber. Most scary of these is the double-ended type, much favoured by gay men – he sticks one end up his butt, and you stick the other inside you, and away you go. It's touching, it really is.

ANAL BEADS

A lovely thought. Anal beads, however, are capable of driving him mad with excitement – so, if you can overcome your natural alarm at the prospect, it may be worth a try. They are simply a little string of differently sized beads, which, when lubricated, you push up his anus – remembering to keep hold of one end, naturally. Then, when he's close to orgasm, you simply pull like a magician whisking a tablecloth away and leaving the plates intact – and the sudden rush of sensation around his prostate will, theoretically, triple the power of his orgasm. You can also use beads

– which rely on the embroidery-silk principle – to pull gently through your labia, so each one bumps against your clitoris. But make sure to wash them first if they've just been up his bum. Mmmm ...

HANDCUFFS

There's nothing wrong with a little role-play. And you can't beat a bit of mild S&M – so long as nobody gets hurt, obviously. If they do, that's real S&M, and you should be in the *News of the World*, being exposed for running a vice ring from your Penzance semi-detached. But if you really don't want to risk your best silk scarves, you need to invest in a pair of handcuffs. I strongly recommend fluffy ones – plain metal are actually quite painful, and despite being marketed as 'sex toys' are more likely to put you in mind of a night in the cells after a drugs bust. So avoid – unless you enjoy very involved role-play, of course. The fluffy ones may make you look like a trussed Muppet, but they'll be far comfier – which is particularly helpful when you lose the key in your excitement.

The best way to use handcuffs is to fasten your arms behind you to the bedhead – when you're sitting up. If you lie down, your muscles will start aching within minutes, and having your arms above your head also has the unfortunate knock-on effect of making your chest look flat. Also, don't pin your arms behind your back when lying down – it will be ridiculously uncomfortable, and rather like having a small, lumpy rucksack strapped to your bum. There is a lot to be said for the excitement of restraint – having him range all over you, without you being able to use your hands to reciprocate, can be highly exciting – but always, without fail, agree first that when you (or he) ask to be released, that's going to happen. You don't want him getting on a power trip, and imagining he's a South American vice cop waiting for a confession. Unless that turns you on, of course.

COCK RINGS

A little device that looks a bit like a ring of fried squid, it simply pops over his erection, and holds all the blood in, thus making it stay harder and last longer. Or that's the idea, anyway. On the other hand, if it's too tight it will simply clamp his penis agonizingly until such time as it turns black and drops off. So it's entirely up to you whether you use one or not.

You can also get rubber sleeves, which are often textured on the inside, which fit over the shaft of his penis, and enhance any handjob by adding to the overall sensation. You may feel these are unnecessary, but at least they don't hurt. They just make his willy look like a baby Dalek.

NIPPLE CLAMPS

Ow. Having said that, many people get off on having little clamps create sensation in their nipples – we all know they have a nerve-hotline to the genitalia, so it figures. The only drawback is, clamps are somewhat painful, to say the least – and you run the risk of feeling like a car being hotwired. Far better to let him pinch them between finger and thumb. That way, at least you don't require jump leads.

where to purchase these items

Ann Summers has a vast range of stock and, rest assured, those assistants really have seen everything. But, if wandering past Chocolate Penises and French maid outfits in broad daylight is too much for you (and last time I went in, some unfortunate guy knocked an entire stand of vibrators over, and remained rooted to the spot with horror for several agonizing moments, so I can see why it might be), they have a mail-order catalogue – it's all terribly discreet, your parcel won't arrive with 'EXTRA LARGE DILDO' stamped on the front, or anything – so it's worth a go. If you want a female-friendly sex shop, try Sh!, in London, (just off Old Street) which is all pink and cosy, and full of pleasant women musing over different kinds of lubrication. Every town has a bog-standard sex shop, and you won't raise eyebrows by going in – but you might die of nerves, plucking up courage to push open that chipped door with 'Adult XXX Fun' written over it. Which is why the Internet's so useful – just type in the sort of thing you want, '+ uk,' and a stockist will magically appear. Make sure it's a secure-server Web site before you give your details, though – and, just a tip, type NOT XXX, NOT busty lesbians, NOT hot hardcore action, as well, if you want to avoid 10,000 useless hits popping up unannounced.

DIY

There is a simple way to avoid the potential nightmare of sex-toy shopping – and that's by engaging in a little DIY. Your home is remarkably full of useful items that can be pressed into service to give you orgasms – but you need to know what is and isn't likely to work, before you can embark on your Domestic Sex-raid. And here are the things you can't manage without ...

GLOVES AND SCARVES

The skin is a highly sensitive organ, and responds remarkably perkily to being touched and caressed with a wide variety of textures. So collect as many types of gloves as you can – ideally, velvet, fur, marabou-trimmed and leather, though if you aren't that glamorous, you may have to make do with woolly, string-backed and fluffy mittens, which aren't quite so sexy. Then blindfold him with your scarf (silk is better than wool, or he'll be pouring with sweat within seconds) and use the different textures to stroke different areas of him. Then he can do the same to you. And if that gets dull, you can always use the scarves to tie each other up.

FRUIT AND VEG

You'll never look at your greengrocer in the same light again. If wooden dildos and plastic vibrators aren't your thing, you need only glance as far as the fruit bowl for a perfectly decent alternative. Well, that's if you keep your cucumbers in the fruit bowl. Vegetables may not appear on the surface to be desperately sexy – after all, nobody fantasizes about aubergines. But, once scrubbed, they can provide a fascinating penis-substitute for the adventurous woman. Obviously, the cucumber is favourite, resembling as it does, the Jolly Green Giant's willy after a course of Viagra. You can either use it yourself, or allow your boyfriend to gently insert it inside you, as long as he isn't going through an insecure patch. I need hardly say 'careful' but don't get carried away, as these things really are large. And make sure it's absolutely clean – the last thing you want is a bunch of fly-killing pesticides up your private parts.

Other useful veg include courgettes – almost alarmingly penis-like, and slightly more manageable than cucumbers. And corn on the cob is simply wasted as a vegetable – in fact, it's so good they actually make vibrators in the shape of it. You may even fancy a dalliance with a clean carrot. However, you can afford to steer clear of potatoes and onions, and, really, there's nothing erotic about balancing mushrooms on your nipples either. So having raided the veg rack (and please, no, don't be thrifty by making a stew afterwards) you may get more fun out of fruit – the big bonus is, you can actually eat fruit off each other and it tastes nice, unlike raw vegetables.

Fruit play

Fruit provides the sex toys of the natural world, by being soft, appealing, non-poisonous and edible. So, in truth, any fruit you fancy can be pressed into service on your (or his) body. But some – such as strawberries – are a little more easily managed than large apples, say, or a whole pineapple. Ideal fruits include melon – though not watermelon, or you'll be picking pips out of your crevices for weeks – cherries, raspberries, bananas (peeled), tangerine segments, seedless grapes, peaches, mangoes, and kiwi fruits. Unerotic ones are Granny Smiths, giant oranges, pears, pomegranates and grapefruits.

So, when you've assembled your fruit basket of love, all you have to do is cut small slices, and place them on each other's erogenous zones. He can eat strawberries out of your vagina – but don't let them get lost up there – you can stack pineapple rings on his willy and nibble them off, he can trail melon over your nipples ... the possibilities are endless. If you do feel the need to insert anything, a banana is the obvious one – but a) make sure it's peeled first, and b) for God's sake, don't let it break off up there by shoving it too far. If you're prone to any kind of inflammations or infections – oh, this is pleasant, this – then don't put anything unusual up there at all, because it's really not worth the bother of having to go to your doctor and explain about the raspberry pips wedged in your labia, is it?

SHOWER HEAD

For DIY sex – and really, getting both of you in the shower is terribly time-consuming and just a whole lot of hassle you don't need – it's time you focused on your shower head. This works best, needless to say, if you happen to have a dynamic power-shower with adjustable spray, rather than a weary trickle that veers from hot to cold every four seconds and stops altogether when your flatmate turns the tap on. Assuming it's workable, however, all you have to do is stand in the shower, legs apart, and angle the head so it's pointing a firm-yet-fine spray at your bits. That's *at*, never *up* – you really don't want high water pressure shooting up you. But once it's the correct speed and temperature, you should soon start to feel a strange but not unpleasant sensation. Ah yes, that must be it – it's the greatest orgasm you've ever had, and all thanks to your shower. Finish with your man, and take to the bathroom. Maybe.

OTHER TASTY TREATS

Obviously, there are other foodstuffs and even drink stuffs that can enhance your excitement no end, most usefully, honey – but don't get it on the carpet or the bed, because you will never, ever get it out, no matter how many Mr Muscle products you buy. It's useful, however, for spreading onto each other's bits and/or bottoms and licking off. But if he says, 'I know, you be Tigger and I'll be Winnie the Pooh,' he's a sad, sick individual, and you must leave him immediately.

Other useful substances include ice cream – though go easy, it's damned chilly. However, a mouthful of ice cream, taken before administering a blowjob, can be positively heavenly for him, and not bad for you either if you ensure it's your favourite flavour. There's also yoghurt, though personally I despise it as a sex aid, a) because it makes the sheets smell like off milk, and b) because it's so healthy. It's really not very rock 'n' roll to be smearing each other in virtually fat-free fruit flavours; you may as well boil up a mug of calorie-free Cup-a-Soup while you're at it.

If you do want to embrace the spirit of rock 'n' roll, however, you cannot go wrong with champagne, whether drinking or pouring it on each other. The bubbles in it can add no end of thrill to your bits, by prickling them lightly, and it'll free your inhibitions by getting you riotously drunk. As I say, you can't lose. But don't be tempted to use the bottle as a sex aid – you don't want to create some kind of internal vacuum and end up in the casualty ward trying to construct a convincing story.

household objects not to try

1. Paperclips on nipples – Painful, silly, and you'll look like a piece of stationery.
2. Bottles – See vacuum problem, above. Not to mention accidental breakages, chipped bits, loose screw-caps …
3. Toast – Never take toast anywhere near your sleeping quarters unless you want to itch for the next six weeks.
4. Roses – Rose petals, fine. Proper roses – there will be a thorn you've overlooked. And greenfly.
5. Melted chocolate – Sounds good, looks appalling. Puts you in mind of horrible accidents in old folk's homes. Really not advisable.
6. Melted wax – Sounds good, feels appalling. If you want agonizing pain and a fried epidermis, you've definitely come to the right place.
7. Pets – Enough said.
8. Clothes line (for tying up) – It won't come undone. Ever.

9. Ice cubes – Freezing, wet, damp patches all over the bed. Like sleeping with frogs.
10. Plastic bags – Because you'll suffocate, stupid.

CHAPTER TEN

Fantasies

Sex between two people is a beautiful thing – between five, it's fantastic.

Woody Allen

One of the most difficult areas of sex to explain – aside from 'Why are you having it with my mother?' obviously – is fantasy. It's such a private issue, and the triggers that turn individuals on are so wildly different, that many women never admit their sexual fantasies at all, partly through embarrassment, and partly through a desire to hold something back for personal use only. This is fair enough, in all honesty. There's nothing more nerve-racking than your boyfriend turning to you and saying, 'So what are you thinking about?' just as you've mentally got the Arab prince riding naked into the tent, waving his ceremonial sword aloft. Or worse, your boyfriend's best mate showing you exactly what he can do with a bar of soap. And do you really want to know what he has planned with Liz Hurley and those thigh-length boots? Exactly. Having said that, this does not mean that fantasy is anything to be ashamed of – and for many women (and to a slightly lesser extent, men) they're an essential part of the sexual experience. Indeed, some can't get turned on without them.

why women need fantasies

For a start our sexual brains are not unlike our sexual organs – the centre is neatly folded away, it needs time and encouragement to get it up and running, and requires subtle stimulation before it unfolds and reveals itself. Whereas being preprogrammed to spill that seed at all costs, a man's sexual centre is leaping up at the first sign of interest like a sniffer dog after heroin. So it doesn't take a lot of mental effort to get him going. If men's sexual imaginations were that good, porn barons would be living in hovels, rather than the mansions they actually inhabit. Women's erotic responses, however, are largely controlled by their mental state. So, while all a man has to think is 'Stockings! Arse!' to generate an erection like the Leaning Tower of Pisa, we need a lot more mental stimulation to get our own erotic floorshow up and running.

We are far less visually stimulated than men (do you recall a female Picasso? No, exactly.) So, while their sexual thrills are triggered mainly by sight (see 'lovely Kimberley, aged 18, loves to sunbathe naked' as proof), ours are not pumped up to the max by the sight of a hairy willy. Which is why our imaginations kick in so readily, should sex appear to be on the horizon. Because, however turned on we are, we can always enhance the actual experience by envisaging a roomful of lustful men watching us pole-dance, or a guy who looks like an actor we vaguely fancy taking us across the bonnet of a Pontiac Firebird somewhere in the desert. Or whatever your personal fantasy happens to be.

should you tell him?

The big problem here is that most men are simple creatures, and certainly not prey to the dark complexities of the female brain. So they tend to assume that if you fantasize about something, that generally means you'd like to do it in real life. Their fantasies tend to be basic, feasible scenarios that could – with a lot of luck and a ton of plastic surgery – actually happen to them. Things like 'Two blonde sisters have sex with me every which way' or 'I get my girlfriend to wear that see-through thing and we do it in the kitchen'. That kind of stuff. You, however, are capable of infinitely more detailed scenarios, beginning with the kind of knickers you're wearing, and ending with the wallpaper design in the bar where you're stripping for dollars. But the big difference is, you wouldn't always be that happy to put your fantasies into practice. Particularly if they involve violence, coercion, or simply 12 Hell's Angels taking their turn with you in a moonlit car park. In reality, you'd be punching 999 into your mobile, and fighting the greasy bastards off, but in fantasy you're merely reclining on the back of a Harley, murmuring 'Oh, you're so big' to the triumphant gang leader. Which brings me neatly to the dilemma of what to do if your boyfriend asks.

The fact is, he may theoretically believe you when you say, 'But it's just a fantasy, it means nothing.' But you can't ensure that he won't spend the next month miserably trying to envisage your gang-bang and wondering if just one man will ever be enough for you. And, what's more, it isn't necessarily any of his business – you may have a wide variety of private fantasies which you really don't feel the need to share. Sometimes, knowing that he knows can ruin the enjoyment, and make you feel silly. And sometimes, he can get really offended – 'My best mate? My bloody *brother*? In the name of God, woman!'

Ultimately, it's helpful to have a fantasy-lie on standby, something fundamentally harmless, which you can trot out, should he whisper, 'What are you thinking about?' and you don't want to squeak, 'Nothing!' unconvincingly. Something about the two of you making passionate love on a deserted beach should do it. Or perhaps a period-drama Mr Darcy fantasy, about him taking you in the bushes, wearing breeches and a ripped shirt. For kindness' sake, it's better to involve him, even if you've secretly invented a gawping crowd of onlookers as well.

If you feel you must be honest, and tell him the whole truth, even if it doesn't involve him, do it gently. And keep repeating 'It's not real, I wouldn't want to do this in real life', like a mantra. And a final word of warning – if it involves his best friend, his brother, or his dad, just don't tell him at all. Ever. Under any circumstances.

should you ask him his?

Men's fantasies are a little more basic than women's. We may start off thinking 'Hmm, I wonder what it would be like to do it with a matador in the middle of a bullring? Well, let's see, there'd be screaming crowds and stampeding bulls ... then again, that's not really safe. Talking of safe, did I lock the windows before I came to bed? There was that thing in the paper about the maniac – oh dear, better go and check.' Before you know it, the moment's gone. This is because we were made to stoke the fire, stop the babies falling into it, knock up a stew and sew the loincloths simultaneously, while the men were made simply to slaughter bison, which took up a lot of concentration. And it's the same with sex.

But men engage in fantasy, not to stir their ailing member into some kind of action, but to provide a fast-track route to satisfaction the moment it's nudged. They don't think, on the whole, about the emotions they'd like to be feeling and they don't furnish a fantasy background for their fantasy woman, unless it's Silicone Valley. So it's likely his fantasy is going to be fairly gruntingly basic – 'threesome', say, or 'loads of horny women crawling all over me'.

If you gaze into his eyes during foreplay and whisper, 'What are you thinking, darling?', he will feel compelled to reply, 'Oh, just about how lovely you are, cuddle-bum.' This is because he knows he can't say, 'Well, I was kind of imagining your best friend tied up, with her beautiful tits straining against the cruel rope,' because if he does you will kill him and leave him, in that order. He may even insist that he doesn't have fantasies, that you are enough. He has learned, rightly, to fear female insecurity as a vengeful and mighty goddess, and will go out of his way to avoid getting into a 'No, fine, think what you want, I'm just a bit surprised, I suppose' conversation that involves you getting increasingly frosty and ends with you whisking round the bedroom gathering up your clothes. So, if you really think that knowing what he fantasizes about will enhance your relationship, pick your moment with extreme care – and even if you don't entirely believe him, let it lie, will you? There is no benefit in knowing that he's envisaging giving all your mates a right good going-over, unless you're a masochist. Of course, the chances are that won't be his fantasy – and he may be only too happy to inform you of exactly what it is, so he can persuade you to act it out. And that's where it can really go pear-shaped ...

should you ever act out fantasies?

It entirely depends what the fantasy is – but be aware, first and foremost, that what works mentally seldom translates brilliantly to real life. As he'll find, when he sees you standing there in the nurse's outfit, blushing furiously, and woodenly stammering 'Please turn over, I must examine you now ...'

Any fantasy that involves other people is almost certainly out. While the idea of swinging like pendulums may be a turn-on, the reality is a bunch of middle-aged accountants tentatively groping each other on a Dralon sofa. Please, keep it an erotic thought. And threesomes lead more often to insane jealousy and despair than they do to wild, uninhibited orgasm. There are compromises, however – such as videoing yourselves at it – that can be a turn-on, without risking relationship meltdown.

If he does want to put fantasy into practice, you must talk it through first; otherwise you'll find yourself halfway down the motorway dressed as a French maid, without a script, and it's likely to end in disaster – or helpless giggling, at any rate. It helps to know exactly what the scenario is, who you're supposed to be, and what sort of thing you're both going to say and do. If you're expecting a 17th-century lord to be gentle and charming to your heaving-bosomed maid, and he sees his role as barking, 'Down on your knees, you filthy whore,' the whole thing's going to fall apart in a shower of tears and recriminations.

If the fantasy has any S&M or violent elements you need to tread very carefully indeed. You absolutely must agree a word that means 'Stop', without fail – and if you're being tied up, never put anything round your neck, and don't let him tie your wrists too tightly. Forced-, or rough-sex fantasies, whilst relatively common, can be genuinely highly upsetting when enacted, so these are really best left to your imagination. The same goes for pain fantasies – it's dangerous ground, and it can very easily go too far and hurt you far more than you ever intended – so avoid anything extreme, unless you're convinced it's right for you.

Obviously don't ever agree to take part in a fantasy scenario you aren't entirely happy or comfortable with – if he's begging you to go out in a fur coat with no underwear, or allow his mate to join you both, you're well within your rights to tell him to get stuffed. Unless that idea really floats your boat, obviously. But if the fantasy does appeal to you both, and if it's more complex than simply 'doing it outside', you may need to consider your feelings towards role-playing. Remember the school play? Well, it's like that, only sexier ...

role-play

This may work better for your man than you, because of the old 'visual trigger' thing. Plus the fact that he simply looks foolish in fancy underwear, whilst you look hot. However, if you want him dressed up as a fireman, or a Chippendale, for that matter, who's he to complain?

After all, role-play has several uses – it can rid you of inhibitions by allowing you to take on the characteristics of another type of woman (my, it's like a Theatre Workshop in here ... feel your character's pain ... know her thoughts ... actually, no, don't – just dress up like her). Obviously, we're talking another sexy woman here. The obvious types include sexy businesswoman, naughty nurse (look, I know, but men are very predictable, OK?), maid, stripper, hooker, or simply glamorous stranger. Oh, and schoolgirl. But make sure he's a decent guy before you go along with that particular fantasy, and if he asks you to call him 'Master' (or, worse, 'Daddy') you'd be better off putting on a tracksuit instead, and running for your life.

Don't get too bogged down with the script – he doesn't want you hovering in the doorway, asking, 'What's my motivation here?' – you just need a few useful phrases such as 'So what qualifies you for this job?' or 'Where does it hurt – show me' or 'I've been very naughty…' It's quite simple, once you get started; the only trick is not laughing.

Once you're up and running, however, you may be surprised by quite how uninhibited you feel – after all, you aren't yourself, you're a Bad Nurse. Though it's also feasible that you'll simply feel damn silly, in which case put on a dressing gown and chalk it up to experience. Even if you have just spent £50 at Ann Summers.

Of course, if either of you decide you can't function without the dressing-up experience, you have taken things too far. Lock the costumes away for a while, and remind yourself that sex can be fun, even if you're not impersonating a sexually overwrought company director. Yes, it can. Really.

talking dirty

There are other ways of enjoying shared fantasies (oh here we go, getting all Californian self-help manual again …) that don't involve scratchy nylon costumes and dog-eared Erotic Scripts. Such as Talking Dirty. This can, of course, take any form you want – from a simple 'Oh God, it's huge!' to 'Fill me with your hot love-spunk, tiger', taking in all manner of by-ways along the journey. Most people find sexy talk a turn-on – but it does depend somewhat on what he says, and how giggly you're feeling. To some women, 'Oh yeah, baby, suck my cock' is a gigantic turn-on, whilst to others, it's merely a hilarious and woeful imitation of a moustachioed 1970s porn star.

When you embark on talking dirty it can, admittedly, be hopelessly embarrassing if you're the kind of girl who never normally goes further than a small gasp every now and then. But a lot of men love to engage in pornographic chit-chat in bed, and if you can bring yourself to tell him what turns you on, you may find it adds a whole new dimension to sex. Particularly if you have thin walls and nosy neighbours.

Start by simply telling him when it feels nice – or where you'd like him to touch you (try to do this in an erotic , 'Mmm, that's so great' way, however, rather than barking like a traffic cop). Once you've mastered that, you can progress to slightly raunchier conversation – but while 'Stick it in me harder' may be acceptable and thrilling, if he expects you to say 'Fill my cunt with your hot spunk, baby' he may be in for a tragic disappointment. On the whole, though, men tend to be rather taken aback, not to say emasculated, if you suddenly get filthier than a toilet wall when they're not prepared. For us, and for them, it's less off-putting to start with a bit of intimate commentary that's sexy without resembling a hardcore rap.

Breaking the initial barrier can be as simple as asking, 'Does this feel nice?' or 'What do you want me to do?' And if you've always called a penis a Widgy, there's no harm in saying 'cock' instead once in a while. Unless you're from Blackburn, in which case it's merely a term of endearment used by grannies.

The fantasy element also comes into talking dirty, because you can describe what's turning you on mentally, as he licks, or thrusts, away. Though don't get carried away, and confess the role your boss is energetically playing in your mental proceedings, whatever you do.

The main drawback is if he's saying things that make you either uncomfortable or amused. If he's whispering, 'Take it all, you filthy whore,' you have to admit that this is slightly less sexy than discussing tax returns. Do it nicely, however – there's no bigger comedown than having your most intimate sexual fantasies mocked. So simply say, 'I know it works for you, but do you think you could tone it down a little because it's not really my fantasy ...' And he should feel free to say the same to you, should your own tide of verbal filth fail to turn him on.

useful things he can say

'I want to go down on you till you come.' (Thoughtful but exciting.)
'I have to fuck you now.' (Urgent and earthy.)
'God, you give me such a hard-on.' (Reassuring.)
'I'm going to screw you senseless.' (Dramatic and full of promise.)

worst things he can say

'Oh, God, baby, suck my cock.' (The movie contract's in the post.)
'Tell me what I'm doing to you.' (Why? Don't you know?)
'Does it feel big? Tell me how big it feels inside you.' (If you need affirmation, see a therapist.)
'I'm going to fuck you till you beg for mercy.' (Not a particularly pleasant thought, is it?)

fantasies worth acting out

THE STRANGERS FANTASY

You both pre-arrange a place to meet – usually a hotel bar – and, on arrival, pretend to chat each other up. After a few drinks, during which you must not let the act slip, you leave for the hotel room you booked earlier, where you have passionate sex, still in 'stranger' character. All the excitement of a one-night stand, none of the infidelity.

WHY NURSE, I HAVE A PAIN ...

The doctors-and-nurses scenario is old but good – works every time. It helps if you dress up, but you don't have to – you can simply take it in turns to examine each other, and rub the pains better. And the good thing is, you can do whatever you like, because you're a highly trained medical professional who knows what's best.

MAID AND MASTER

You have to be in a subservient mood for this one – but if you normally boss him about and earn twice as much, it can make a nice change. Not one to try, perhaps, if you're the office junior and he's the chairman – it's a little too subservient under those circumstances. All you have to do, however, is construct a French maid's outfit (black mini, apron), buy a feather duster, and commence to dust, while he barks orders, which become increasingly questionable. Come on, it's the only chance he'll ever get ...

JOB INTERVIEW

Of course, in reality there's absolutely nothing sexy about a job interview – you'll be sweating from nerves, not passion. But in the bedroom, you wearing a foxy business suit and a pair of glasses can work wonders, as you quiz him on his love credentials. 'Of course, we'll need a practical demonstration of your talents' is always a useful line. And do remember to take his number if he comes up to scratch.

OUTSIDE

Sex outdoors is a favourite fantasy for men and women – and it can be fantastic, if you choose somewhere that's a) deserted and b) warm. Say, a lonely beach at the height of summer – though there's not many of those around. Or a sunlit woodland glade – again, not too common in cities. You may strike lucky, and find a field, but watch for irate farmers, and cows nibbling at your underwear. Basically, sex outdoors is a lottery – if you find the right location, it'll be amazing; if you don't, you'll find yourself in the local paper.

fantasies not worth acting out

S&M

Painful, and prone to dislodging deep-seated emotional angst that you never knew you had, related to abandonment, pain and humiliation. You may need long-term therapy afterwards. So only do this if you're determined to restrict things to a bit of light bondage, rather than traumatic master–slave punishment sessions, OK?

THREESOMES

Oh God, NO. Unless you are both the most secure couple in the world (and if Tom and Nicole can split, no one's safe), never introduce a third party into your sex sessions. Even if they're a stranger. Even if they're your best friend. There will be jealousy and pain involved, guaranteed. And no hot all-night session with two writhing blondes is worth that. No, it isn't. Fine, try it yourself if you must, and you'll see I'm right. (Though if you're absolutely determined, skip ahead to Kinky Sex ...)

SUPERHEROES

For some reason, many sex shops sell Superman or Batman costumes. This is largely as erotic as dressing up like Rupert the Bear, or Orville the Duck. It just doesn't work. While George Clooney as Batman had a certain charm, your boyfriend in a stretchy helmet with bat ears is going to look like Del Boy on his way to a fancy-dress party. It's particularly unerotic if he dives from the top of the wardrobe, and breaks the bed – or your ribs. If you truly fantasize about being rescued, have him dress as a fireman, for God's sake.

IN PUBLIC

Well, it's illegal, for a start – you could be prosecuted for obscenity. Sneaking into the pub loos for a quickie is one thing, but getting it on it broad daylight in the middle of the shopping precinct is quite another. So, while you may entertain fantasies regarding you shagging on a snooker table while the pub regulars look on, in reality you'll be chucked out and barred, not to mention humiliated. Because in fantasy you can edit all the bad bits; in real life – you can't.

ON A PLANE

Many people nurture thoughts of joining the mile-high club. If you have a private Lear jet, it's a great plan. If you're going economy class to Malaga, however, it ain't. For a start, how are the two of you going to get into the loo, when it involves passing 52 boozed-up tourists, who will feel no embarrassment when it comes to passing comment? And, once you get there, there's bound to be turbulence, and you'll either have to rush back to your seats or risk braining yourselves on the sink. And then there's the toddler waiting patiently outside, who can't hold on much longer ... Just don't go there.

CHAPTER ELEVEN

Masturbation

The nice thing about masturbation is that you don't have to dress up for it.

Truman Capote

They used to say masturbation would make you go blind. If that were the case, most of the population would be tapping around with white sticks – because almost everyone does it. And, while fewer women than men who are in relationships claim to indulge, it's a fair bet that most of them are lying.

When you're single, masturbating is the best chance you're going to get of a sex life – and it also cuts out all risk of unpleasant diseases, embarrassment, and fear that he won't phone afterwards. When you're not, however, it remains a handy snack, for when you don't want a full meal – that is, you really want a quick, tension-releasing orgasm, but you really can't be bothered with all the kissing and rolling round that accompanies sex with your partner. He, of course, feels the same way – but a surprising number of women refuse to believe that masturbation isn't some kind of betrayal, insisting, 'If he loves me, why does he need to do it on his own?' Because it's quick and efficient when he does it on his own, that's why – and if he just wants to be briefly self-interested and come, to rid himself of the erotic stirrings he's occasionally plagued with, then whyever not? You wouldn't thank him if he dragged you home from work just to give him a handjob, would you?

The problem is, it's still common to see masturbation as a slightly shameful act. It's probably the one sexual topic that women don't discuss with each other. Which is fine – personally, I don't need to know which of my friends uses a vibrator, either – but that doesn't mean it isn't a useful and, indeed, delightful thing to do, when for whatever reason partner sex isn't happening.

how to do it

Fiddling with your bits usually does the trick. However, if you want to get a little more complex – it depends whether you want a quick tension-relieving orgasm, or the full sex-replacement experience. If it's the first option, the simplest way is to remain fully dressed apart from your knickers – unless you're wearing trousers; in which case, simply whisk them to one side – and if you have privacy, use a vibrator – which of course, you now own, having read and digested the Sex Toys chapter in full. Start by holding it lightly against you on slow speed, and, as things become pleasantly hazy (around 30 seconds later), flick it to fast – it's kind of like remembering to change gears on PlayStation driving games. With luck and some concentration on the most relevant fantasy scenario from your mental erotic flip-chart, you should have a fairly impressive orgasm in under two minutes. This only works, however, if you're alone in the house – otherwise the gentle buzzing will alert everyone within a three-mile radius that you're masturbating. Say you suddenly come over all sensual in the middle of the office, and feel compelled to nip to the loo for instant relief? (Then I'd say you were a braver woman than me, but that's beside the point.) You need to use your fingers – and stay silent at all costs, do you hear? This isn't *Ally*

McBeal, you know. The quickest way is to lick them, then use two fingers to rub in small circles over your clitoris. Some women also like to touch their nipples with their other hand. If you can contrive to ignore gossiping colleagues banging in and out of adjacent cubicles, you should manage an orgasm within a few minutes, and be able to return to your desk fully rejuvenated, if slightly vague. Just make sure that if the fire alarm goes off mid-orgasm, you tuck yourself in properly and do all your buttons up.

SLOWLY

Slow masturbating is arguably a more rewarding experience, as it can offer a little of the sensual thrill of sex, whilst allowing you to remain entirely selfish, and unconcerned with anyone's pleasure but your own. Certain sexperts suggest that you prepare your bedchamber like some sort of tantric goddess's love nest before beginning, with candles and silk drapes and the like, but I'd merely advise you to dim the lights slightly, put the answerphone on, and make sure you can hear the key well in advance, if you have flatmates who may suddenly decide to pop home. Bed is the most obvious and comfortable place for a little self-exploration, but you may prefer to sit on a chair – or even in front of a mirror, because if you're a bit of a narcissist, having a good, pornographic look at all your own bits and pieces can be something of a turn-on. I wouldn't suggest you go as far as Betty Dodds, however, who, as an original American feminist, runs masturbation workshops, where women of all shapes and sizes whip off all their clothes and get down, in broad daylight and in front of each other. Unless you're feeling particularly free and open, though, it may be better to do this alone.

This sort of masturbation is very good for the less experienced woman, who may not know exactly what she wants her lovers to do – so by finding out herself, it makes life easier for them when it comes to touching her the right way.

It's always nice to start off with a bath – indeed, it's always nice to have a little go in the bath. But if you do, make sure you don't get scented soap up your parts, as you will be in agony, and you're more likely to spend the evening perched on a ice pack than learning the intimate secrets of your body. Unscented soap, however, makes a handy aid to masturbation, if you simply rub it over your clitoris. Other women swear by flannels to rub against, and still others actually purchase vibrating sponges, which are apparently not dangerous – you just get in the water, clutch them between your legs, and away you go. But I don't know how you'll explain to your flatmate why your bath sponge keeps buzzing. The bath does offer a golden opportunity for breast-fondling if you go for that, and also provides you with a lockable room in which to do your experimenting. All the same, if you prefer to be dry before you embark on your quest, stay naked after you get out of the bath, and lie down on a pile of towels – ideally, white, fluffy ones, not your boyfriend's 'Surfers Do It Standing Up' beach towel – and massage scented body lotion into your skin, all over – or as all over as you can manage, given that you haven't got arms like Mr Tickle. This is not the time to be thinking, 'Christ, I can't believe how flabby my stomach's got' or 'By God, my thighs are like logs'. You're supposed to be feeling good about yourself. If at all possible, try to look at yourself as a bloke might see you: not your sneering, inadequate ex; we're talking about a nice, lust-crazed bloke who fancies the pants off you. As all the agony aunties say, 'Focus on the positives' – your nice skin, or your finely shaped kneecaps. Whatever, as long as it makes you feel good about yourself. At this point, you may want to drum up a fantasy of some sort – run through a few scenarios mentally, to see which one works best, first, because there's nothing worse than getting halfway through a hot 'virgin sacrifice' fantasy, only to realize you aren't enjoying it, and having to quickly construct a whole 'naughty schoolgirl' situation to replace it before you go off the boil altogether.

Run your hands over your body, paying particular attention to anywhere that feels excitable. Try different touches, fingernails only, or whole-hand movements, and feel free to play with your breasts – if men had them, they'd never leave the house. Then allow a hand to drift down to your clitoris. Some women like to insert something inside themselves at the stage – a vibrator, a finger, a baby carrot; whatever turns you on, just as long as it's hygienic. If you're serious about this penetration lark, you may wish to put a condom over the vibrator (or carrot) to remind you of a real willy. Others, however, simply stimulate their clitoris. If you're not entirely familiar with orgasming regularly, just fiddle around till you find a touch that suits you – and make sure you're wet enough to be able to stroke without dragging the skin, or it'll never work.

After that, it ought to come pretty naturally – and once you come, the good thing is you can do it all again, without waiting for anyone to rustle up another erection.

when he masturbates

If your bloke says he doesn't masturbate, there's a good chance he's not being entirely truthful – unless you're having sex every day and he's exhausted. Because most blokes feel the need, whether frequently or occasionally, to offload a little of their sperm-stockpile. And, unless you're a particularly willing partner with no job or commitments, there's bound to be times when you're not around and he feels the need.

It may not be the greatest thought ('Where does he do it? On the sheets? – Argh!'), but equally, there's little point feeling resentful or upset by it – it is not, repeat, NOT, a form of infidelity. You may torture yourself fretting over what he thinks about during his quick pull, but the chances are it's nothing more sinister than the last time you had sex together. Maybe your arse in a G-string. He really isn't going to go to the trouble of creating mental football teams of blonde beauties when he's got one minute to have an orgasm before he's late for work.

For him, it's much more of a physical release than a sensual experience. He knows exactly how to handle his penis for the quickest results, like getting a well-schooled horse round a familiar series of jumps. It doesn't mean that he doesn't prefer it when you do it for him – but when he wants quick, painless relief, as the cold remedy ads say, he can't beat a quick hand-shuffle. There's no reason for you to get jealous, unless he's masturbating when you're in the bed next to him. In which case, either ask if you can watch (you might pick up some tips), or ask him why he prefers to sort himself out. There's only one other potential problem, though, and it's a biggie. That age-old bone of contention – porn.

porn and why he likes it

In all honesty, there's barely a man alive who hasn't, at some point, experienced some form of pornography. However great a feminist you are, however repulsive the idea of women being exploited in the name of cheap sexual gratification, however ardently your man appears to agree with you – it's almost certain that at some stage he will have been panting heavily over the image of a nubile young bird with her tits (and, probably, bits) out. That doesn't necessarily mean that his Ikea bedside cabinet is stuffed with dog-eared copies of *Razzle* any more – but it helps if you bear in mind that men are, fundamentally, programmed to respond favourably to pictures of naked women. As they get older, those men may decide that, yes, it is exploitative, and prefer to get their kicks trying to spot fleeting glimpses of breasts in Channel 4 art-house movies – but it doesn't change the basic fact that men like looking at ladies' bits. And if yours aren't readily available, they'll make do with looking at someone else's.

This is a remarkably unappealing fact for us to grasp – I too would infinitely prefer it if my partner remained profoundly uninterested in anyone's breasts but mine. But even if he only gives a passing flicker of acknowledgement, breasts are configured to excite his interest. And, given that men are sexually aroused by visual stimulation, it's not surprising that the majority would argue than porn is a useful aid to orgasm. Only you can decide whether you're prepared to permit it playing a part in your relationship, if he does want to use it. He may have assumed you'd go ballistic, and hidden it – or he may simply have outgrown the desire for it altogether. If not, it helps to know what it generally involves – and we're talking legal porn here, featuring grown men and women performing acceptable acts, not degrading filth that the vice squad would carry away in clear envelopes. If he owns any of that stuff, then you may well want to consider what kind of guy you're mixed up with ... but Mr Normal will probably be dealing in a mild form of one of the following types.

PRINTED PORN

The old school of porn – cheap, glossy paper, beaver shots, not many words. Lovely. Titles include *Men Only*, *Razzle*, *Club International* and, for the more specialist man, *Asian Babes*. For the more pensioner-oriented guy, there's even *60 Plus*, but let's not go there for now. This is almost certainly the porn on which your guy was sexually weaned as an adolescent, so he may well harbour a nostalgic fondness for it. It's generally fair, harmless, though from a female point of view fairly depressing – most of the girls look like they were plucked from hanging round the bus shelter smoking, then given a cheap perm and some plastic earrings and told to spread 'em. In fact, chances are, that's exactly what happened. Print porn has a high jealousy rating, however, as it tends to feature willing-looking women, alone, therefore creating a certain exclusivity during your boyfriend's bathroom wanks. If you need cheering up, however, check out *Readers' Wives*, and reassure yourself that, if they're fanciable, you're Elle Macpherson in comparison.

INTERNET

The Internet has totally changed the way porn is supplied – and not, many would argue, for the better. Whereas once it was necessary for a guy to conceal his jazz-material inside a copy of *Gardening Today* and try not to look like a pervert shuffling out of the shop, he can now download almost any sexual scenario he wishes for, in the privacy of his own home. Sadly, certain individuals, somewhat lacking in what we may choose to call 'having a life' have taken that concept and run with it – which means a fair number of men who spend almost all their free time chasing up new and better Internet porn. Hopefully your guy isn't one of them – but he may well have occasionally typed in 'XXX red-hot lesbians' just to see what would happen. If he is sneaking off to the home computer to 'check the scores' and coming back rather flushed, you may well find that he's been checking the measurements of Kelli from Dallas, 21, instead. The Internet is invasive, and you're perfectly justified in complaining if he's devoting time he could be spending with you to pursuing large-busted Texans on pay-per-view sites. It can become fairly addictive – there's always a better link to follow – so you must make it clear to him if you find his behaviour unacceptable.

MOVIES

Porn movies are perhaps the least worrying and most amusing of all porn: partly because of the percussion-heavy 1970s-style soundtracks, partly because of the hilariously poor scripts ('My radiator's broken, it's so hot!' etc. etc.); and partly simply because watching two fairly average-looking people have sex is horrifyingly fascinating, rather like watching magnified insects doing it. Most men get over porn films at the age of 18 – only to be revisited on boys' nights, and when they're really, really bored. They're more ironic entertainment than pure satisfaction, and, what's more, they often involve men – and your average bloke doesn't want to watch another man's dangly bits wafting in the breeze when he's trying to concentrate on the German bird with the vast knockers. They can, however, offer some fun to couples – it's hard to be jealous of the type of woman who generally features in these things and, even if she is pretty, console yourself with the thought that she's probably got bits like the channel tunnel, and only five years left of her chosen career. So if you can bring yourself to watch it with your boyfriend, you may find, to your amazement, that watching naked people at it can be something of a turn-on. Though it does help if you're drunk, and prepared to check your sense of humour in at the door.

Ultimately, it's your prerogative to decide whether you can accept him using porn. If you're prepared to give it a go – and he accepts it, of course – it may be worth joining in, by looking at it with him (though spitting 'nice earrings, pig-face' at every turn of the page may not enhance anyone's enjoyment). Alternatively, if you are in a long-term, trusting relationship – and I can't emphasize that strongly enough – consider letting him either take Polaroids of you in somewhat abandoned positions, or even video you both having sex. It can be a fantastic replacement for porn – as long as you know exactly where the incriminating evidence is kept, and have full control over it. Don't even consider this option if you think there's a chance he'll post you off to *Readers' Wives*. Unless that's long been a secret dream of yours, obviously.

women's porn

Given that we are indeed less visual creatures than men, women's porn is a pretty sorry little collection. Brave publishers have occasionally attempted to get us interested in pictures of oiled, grinning, naked men with flaccid willies (because it's still illegal to show erections in Britain – that's fair), but oddly enough they've sold well to the gay population, and women have merely guffawed at the perma-tanned fool with his string bean out, and bought *Playboy* instead. Anyway, a great many women actually find it more stimulating to look at pictures of nude women. More curves, prettier, and don't look like idiots with a bag of turkey giblets stapled to their crotches, you see. So, for us, magazines really don't do it. There are a few mags aimed at couples, featuring erotic stories, and pictures of attractive people galloping to the finish, but it's a limited market, because all the women are intimidatingly pretty and all the men look like gay beefcake. Aside from that, it's great ... Our other alternative is erotic literature.

CLIT LIT

Some bright spark realized some time ago that women are turned on by words, and verbal images that fire their imaginations. So series such as Black Lace were born – soft porn novels, aimed at women, and featuring feisty heroines in a variety of unlikely and erotic situations. The idea is, you read them, imagine yourself in the heroine's place, as the nimble fingers of Sven unlace her straining corsets and play arias of longing on her nipples, and you're well away. Some of them, indeed, are quite sexy – whilst some are merely silly. But, for a handy erotic boost to the imagination, they certainly serve a purpose. The trick is finding one that appeals to you personally – there's no point ploughing through a story about a sexually charged boating holiday if you secretly long to be deflowered by a knight of the Round Table. And the other problem is actually buying them, without looking like a sex-starved spinster who's going home to her cats and her lonely fantasies. Which is why the Internet is so damned handy for ordering books.

FILMS

Well, if you like porn films, you're spoilt for choice. But most are, it has to be said, aimed at the male end of the market. At least, they were, until ex-porn star Candida Royale (wouldn't you love her name?) turned her well-practised hands to directing porn flicks for women. Their big selling point is that they have a plot, and a decent script. So, unlike the man's version ('I've come to fix your washer – oh! oh! Oh!'), you can actually get involved in the story, and the sex is seamlessly woven into that. It's also woman-friendly sex – lots of foreplay, and at least the appearance of caring men who like going down on women for hours. If they don't float your boat ... well, there's always Channel 4 art-house movies, eh?

INTERNET

Want to see what Woody the Cowboy has to offer? No, didn't think so. Unless you can be bothered following the XXX links to erotic stories that are mainly inarticulate Yanks posting their feeble fantasies – 'We went to this, like, party, and Jenny was real horny, and her friend Becky was there, and like, they start licking each other and stuff' – don't bother. Really, I mean it. You could be shopping online in the time you're wasting, honey.

CHAPTER TWELVE

Kinky stuff

I tried phone sex once, but the holes were too small.

Anon

More tea, vicar? Because you may need something to calm you down as we investigate the murky yet oddly exciting world of Kinky Sex. It may be that your sex life has always been a meat-and-two-veg sort of affair, and you have no plans to start nibbling sushi and getting all exotic now. Which is fine – you keep the lights switched off and *Greatest Love Songs Ever* on the stereo, and you have a nice time. Bye. But for those of us who are even mildly intrigued by the possibilities offered by kinky sex, it's worth investigating what the main branches of experimentation involve. We're not talking about anything illegal, painful, or downright obscene, however – if you want to beat a goat till it screams, wearing only a rubber gimp mask, that's your look-out – but I won't be giving you tips on how to catch farmyard animals, so you're on your own there.

Obviously, it goes without saying that before you embark on any of this you will ensure you're with a lovely, trustworthy partner, who isn't going to thank you for a hot night and jump in a cab next day (unless he already lives with you, and simply prefers to travel by taxi). Otherwise you may well emerge feeling a wee bit depressed. Kinky sex can be fantastic fun, but it can also make you feel very vulnerable if you're not with the right person. And besides – you really don't want to be jumping straight into bed with a guy you've just met who's wielding a cat o' nine tails and a pair of handcuffs.

However, if you're simply on a mission to explore a little more of the sexual world out there with your full-time man, it helps to know what your options are. Or, at least, the options that won't put you in prison.

bondage

Bondage is anything from having your wrists loosely bound with a scarf, to being trussed up like a chicken and tied to a chair with leather straps by your ankles, hands and waist. But whether bondage-lite, or the serious, Tory-MP-style stuff, the basic point is to restrain your movements during sexual activity, and therefore drive you (and your unbound partner) to greater heights of passion. The fact that you can't move fully can be very arousing, both because of the submission involved – letting a partner take all responsibility for what happens can be very liberating – and because lack of movement makes you far more aware of your exposed body. If you've never done it before, be aware that you may not like it, and make sure he's ready to stop the moment you say the word. And never pretend you're enjoying yourself if you feel unpleasantly out of control, in pain, or upset – it's supposed to be fun, not a hideous endurance test. Scarves are gentler than handcuffs – but always use silk or cotton, never nylon, because you really don't want to be lying there with aching arms two hours later, as he attempts to saw through the knots with the bread knife.

When you are tied – and unless you're feeling very confident, it's probably best to start off just tying your hands together, not spread-eagling yourself with each ankle tied to a bedpost – he should entertain himself by going down on you, or caressing you all over, and teasing you by touching your clitoris then returning to your breasts for a while, and alternating till you beg. You can enhance the experience with a blindfold, too – it intensifies the sensations by offering mild sensory deprivation. Don't, however, bother with a gag – that's getting way too *Pulp Fiction* for most.

Of course, you can tie him up, too – and practise slow masturbation in return. A few strokes of a handjob, wait a while, return ... and so on. He will beg like a man in the desert who's glimpsed water – but hold out. Then, when his orgasm finally arrives, it'll be more explosive than Millennium-night fireworks.

You can also straddle him and have sex – again, a winner, and you'll enjoy the feeling of power as he begs and pleads for more. It's slightly more difficult to have sex when you're tied up, unless you have your arms above your head and your legs spread. As I say, a little vulnerable – but if it works for you, don't knock it. You can vary the bondage theme, too, by tying each other to chairs (not at the same time, stupid – how's that going to work?) and going down on each other. Make sure it's a stable chair, though, won't you?

You can, in fact, tie one another to anything – heavy pieces of furniture, bedposts, each other – but perhaps not lampposts, railings and trees, unless you wish to shock passing dog-walkers with your daring.

Needless to say, never, ever tie anything round your neck. You want to have fun, not die in agony.

S&M

S&M stands for 'Sadism and masochism': a lovely twosome. Sadists are people who enjoy inflicting pain, while masochists enjoy receiving it – so indeed, the perfect pairing is one of each. However, only certain people who tend to take it all rather seriously, and spend their weekends visiting suburban dungeons, fall neatly into the 'either/or' category – for most, S&M is sexual experimentation, and roles can be swapped around. But you may not wish to go very far down this route anyway, seeing as the basic point of S&M is pain or, at the very least, submission and domination. Most women don't want to be crawling at their partner's jackboots, chanting 'I'm a worthless slave who must be punished' on a regular basis, so if you are going to introduce S&M into the bedroom, may I suggest a very mild version – that is, the version, that involves leather, masks and whips, but no actual scars, or midnight visits to A&E?

You'll need to purchase some attractive leather (or PVC) wear – which can range from a simple black bra and knickers, to the full catsuit, with holes for breasts, and a studded collar. And that's just for him. If the idea of seeing your nearest and dearest prance around in a black PVC posing pouch studded with spikes doesn't fill you with joy, of course, you can remain naked – but that does kind of miss the point. If you do want to test out the pleasure/pain principle (and S&M-ers are convinced that there's only a thin line between them), then invest in a cat o' nine tails, which is small whip that looks rather like a leather egg-whisk. You don't want to be messing with a proper whip: he's not a race horse and, besides, those things really do hurt.

With your egg-whisk, simply whack it lightly across your partner's bum, increasing the strength of your strokes till he's no longer enjoying it. If, indeed, he ever was in the first place. Remember, though, you are wielding an instrument of torture – so go easy. He can also try it on you – and then rub your bum better with body lotion. Perhaps not the actions of the true S&M fiend, but still ...

You may also want to try a bit of rough sex – which is exactly as it sounds, and involves scratching, biting and pulling at each other. It can be exciting, but only when you're both truly sure than no one's going to get genuinely badly hurt. That's not as easy as it sounds, however – in the heat of passion, your pain receptors are slightly anaesthetized, and what seems like a sexy bite can leave you with a whacking great bruise on your neck. A far safer alternative is using your arms to pin each other down, and having fast, urgent sex, rather than risk scarring each other for life.

I need hardly say that any kind of cutting, blood-letting or asphyxiating is simply stupid and dangerous. It's not big or clever, and I'm not even going to make a joke about it. That's how serious I am.

spanking

It used to be known as the English Vice – because foreigners believed that the only way Englishmen ever got off was through being spanked, having spent six years at public school being beaten senseless with canes by homoerotic prefects. This may no longer be true, but there are still a sizable number of men and women who enjoy a good spanking. Madonna once even wrote a song about it ('Hanky Panky' – which was crap, but that's beside the point). So if you fancy testing its charms, simply whip off your knickers, and position yourself either bent over a chair or the bed, crouching doggy style, or even bent over your bloke's knee. It has to be said, this is not a particularly powerful position to be in, and it does all raise searching feminist questions about violence, domination and submission within your relationship … but, hey, you've nothing better to do on a Tuesday night, and you can always stand up again if you don't like it. Fantasy role-play works very well here – otherwise you're going to feel a bit of a prat, being smacked soundly for no reason whatsoever. A bit of 'Oh, I've been so naughty!', 'Well then, my dear, you must be punished!' may go down a treat. Careful he doesn't get too carried away and start shouting 'Whore! Bitch!' with every slap, though. There is apparently something quite exciting about the gradual heating-up of your arse cheeks and, inevitably, it goes tingly after a few slaps, which you may enjoy. Alternatively, you may well prefer to whack his buttocks with wild abandon – if he lets you, it's quite good therapy. Let it all out, and you'll feel much better afterwards. So might he, especially if he went to public school. Bottom-smacking is, of course, not to be confused with an excuse to show violence towards your partner. Anyone who's not enjoying themselves need to be listened to immediately – and that doesn't mean ignore his pleas for mercy whilst shouting, 'And that's for flirting at that party!', 'And that's for never putting the rubbish out!' That's not the idea at all, is it?

water sports

Now, the innocents amongst you will wonder why surfing is kinky, everyone else will merely shudder in horror – probably. Water sports is, of course, the act of weeing on one's partner. The warmth and intimacy of the act is, for some, a huge turn-on. Though, for everybody else, a packet of disposable nappies is sexier. However, if you want basic guidelines for this rather specialist sport, start with plastic sheeting and a bucket of water. In fact, make preparations as you would for a major building project, and you can't go wrong. You can put the plastic on the bed or floor, and then, simply drink a large glass of water, and wee on your partner, who is lying down. You can aim it at their genitals or their mouth (yum!), or simply trail pretty patterns onto them. Of course, if he's weeing on you, he'll have trouble getting an exact aim, because erections cause wee to go everywhere, like a watering can. And if he's not got an erection, why are you bothering at all? (Look, I'm a sexpert, I'm not allowed to be judgmental, but you know, it's not an attractive picture really, is it?) Afterwards, mop up, and hope to god no one asks what that funny smell coming from the bedroom is.

And if you fancy a bit of degradation, but don't like the sound of the whole plastic sheets situation, do it in the bath. Nice. The only good news is, wee isn't poisonous. So that's alright, then.

threesomes and orgies

Remarkably popular, if you believe the fiction in porn magazines. And, even if you don't, there are enough contact ads in said magazines to convince the casual onlooker than half of Britain spends its weekends swinging with Surrey middle managers called Pat and Ted. This is probably not true – but it does go on. And, if you're convinced that you have a relationship which can withstand bringing other people into it, go right ahead, and ignore all my sensible advice from previous chapters. If you do attempt it, though, it has to be a mutual decision – your bloke piling pressure on you to entertain him by shagging his mate (or your best friend) is not a good start. If you're not both equally keen, forget the whole notion. If you are (and on your head be it, madam), your first task is to pick the third member. Obviously, you have to decide if it's going to be a man or woman – and whether you want to know them or not. Knowing them risks hideous embarrassment afterwards, not to mention your little secret escaping. Not knowing them means that you risk catching nasty diseases, not to mention the general insecurity posed by sharing a very intimate act with a complete stranger. However, if you promise to use condoms, and try to recruit participants whom you know (perhaps via a friend) are not insane, I'd recommend semi-strangers rather than friends – especially if you're involving your boyfriend. But if it's just you, a single slapper out for larks, then you'd better pick two male mates. At least you know they're relatively sane.

If you don't know how to begin your threesome, a good bet – for any kind of sexual warm-up – is always a lot of drink and a forfeit game. Make sure the forfeits involve stripping, kissing, fondling and so on – you're never going to get anywhere if you suggest the loser runs round the room three times singing the theme from *Titanic*. Well, you might get a laugh, but that's all.

After that, you're pretty much on your own – apart from the obvious (USE CONDOMS) and the etiquette issues. Which are, basically, if you've got two people in bed, make sure you devote enough time to each of them – there's nothing worse than two-thirds of a threesome pairing off, and you may as well save yourself the bother if you're going to do that. Of course, if one participant is your boyfriend, be particularly careful about this.

And if you want to keep your relationship intact, a) don't make threesomes a habit, b) don't get emotionally involved with the other participant, and c) don't sleep with them behind your boyfriend's back.

Orgies are somewhat harder to find, and may involve seeking out swingers' clubs in the dingy back streets of small towns, and watching large ladies being half-heartedly whipped by balding men in stained briefs. Then again, you may have a bunch of attractive friends who'd like nothing better than to hold a 1970s-style Key Party, where you all chuck your car keys in a bowl, pick a set out, and sleep with their owner. If you do, there's just two things to remember: collect your own keys at the end of night, or you'll never get home. And when it all falls apart in a shower of sobbing and recriminations, don't say I didn't warn you.

anal sex

Used to be considered less kinky, more of a handy birth-control method. 'One up the bum, none in the tum', as the old saying went – though your Gran may not have mentioned that one. However, despite its appeal, a lot of women remain repelled rather than excited by the idea. For men, it's a winner – unless they have some throwback hang-up about it being 'gay'. It offers a tightness of fit that simply can't be achieved with vaginal sex and, therefore, exceptional friction, which naturally feels fantastic. For women, though, the appeal is often less physical than mental – it's seen as a forbidden area of the body, and to allow him entry to your anus is basically saying 'Take all of me', which can be arousing in itself. However, while men have a prostate gland, which is stimulated by probing their inner recesses, we don't – which is why gay men have so much fun, and lesbians largely tend to leave each other's bums alone.

Anal sex is not first-date material, it has to be said. If you're going to risk pain, and expose yourself physically and, often, emotionally – by allowing your most intimate area to be penetrated, then it helps if you know the guy pretty well. But if you do want to give it a whirl, there are a few things you need to know first. Anal skin tears extremely easily – unlike the vagina, it's made for one-way traffic, and is therefore far less elastic and resilient, so you can bruise and tear far more easily inside if your partner's anything less than gentle. Being so thin, it's also perfect for passing the HIV virus into your body – so for God's sake make sure you use a strong condom.

Before he enters you, use tons of lubrication – not just a pathetic little dab, really use tons – and it helps immensely if you've had enough foreplay to be properly turned on first, otherwise you'll tense up so much he won't be able to get it in at all. Most people are paranoid about cleanliness at this point – so make sure you've been to the toilet beforehand, and washed thoroughly. I know, this is all far too much information, but if you're ever going to do it, you need to know this stuff. It's also vital that he doesn't exit your anus and enter your vagina without changing condoms – if he does, he'll be transferring all manner of bacteria, which can cause you nasty problems later. The same goes for touching with his fingers. Why do you think kids are told to wipe front to back? Because it's hygienic, that's why.

The perfect position for anal sex is, naturally, doggy-style – that way he can see where everything is, and it makes it easier to enter. He should bear in mind that, unlike the vagina, which slopes towards your back, the anus is almost vertical – so he should adjust his thrust accordingly. He must use his fingers or a vibrator to stretch the opening slightly first – and then enter very, very gently. It may be too tight, because you're tense – if so, don't force it because it can really hurt. If it's not, he should just push in as far as he can, and if you feel anything more painful than a strange fullness, he can pull right out again. Keep using lubrication as he thrusts (gently, mind) if it starts to feel dry. He can reach round to your clitoris, and vagina, to play with them too, if he's feeling coordinated enough.

You shouldn't bleed, and it should return to normal almost immediately he pulls out – but if it hurts, or you spot any blood, don't do it again in a hurry. He may have caused an anal fissure (cut) – oh, this is just lovely, this is – which isn't serious but can be painful. And, needless to say, once again, unless you're both 100 per cent sure about doing this, give it a miss. Even if he does beg and plead.

exhibitionism

Exhibitionists like to show off sexually. Voyeurs like to watch. And if you want to introduce these elements into your relationship, you may find you automatically fall into those roles – or maybe you'd prefer to take turns. The trouble is, 'showing off' involves a little more than merely standing on a chair singing, 'Doe, a Deer' like it did when you were six. Exhibitionism tends to imply that you're going to be making a sexual statement in public. So you need to be very careful – standing in the window naked may turn you on, but it won't do the same for your neighbours (unless they're excitable college boys, in which case they'll think they've died and gone to Neighbour Heaven). And, given that prancing around in public is out of the question unless you want to be wrapped in a blanket and taken down the police station, you're going to have to think of less dangerous ways of showing yourself off. This is where Web-cams, videos and cameras come in nicely – if you so desire, you can rig up your computer to show your bedroom, as has Jenni, of Jenni-cam Internet fame. She has millions of fans who log on to see her get dressed and undressed – not to mention clean her teeth, pick her nails ... Of course, you can always switch it off occasionally. Never, ever reply to any emails giving personal details, however – don't even tell them what country you're in. And hope to God nobody recognizes you.

If you and your man both want to be exhibitionists, then video cameras are a good bet – you can film yourselves doing whatever you like and, if you so desire, send the tape to a distribution company and see if they fancy marketing it. Or more sensibly, lock it away so nobody ever sees it but you two. Even watching each other masturbate can satisfy the mild exhibitionist

– and if you're feeling truly daring, you can always try it with the curtains open. Then again, you don't want things to end up like *Confessions of a Window Cleaner*, with randy workmen banging on the glass ... so watch it.

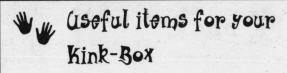

Useful items for your Kink-Box

POLAROID CAMERA

Ideal for snapping those moments of passion – as long as you lock them up afterwards. 'Mum? No! It's nothing!'...

HANDCUFFS/SCARVES

If you use handcuffs, make sure they're fluffy or padded – and don't lose the key.

PLAYING CARDS

Useful for any number of kinky games and forfeits – the best games are Pontoon (21) and poker.

BLINDFOLD

Make sure it's black and silk – nobody looks sexy with a checked woolly scarf tied over their eyes.

WHIP

A small whip is always useful, particularly when accessorized with elbow-length gloves. (Not for him, mind.)

STRONG DRINK

Strong drink is a vital component of the kinky experience – otherwise, how are you ever going to overcome your inhibitions long enough to get going?

CHAPTER THIRTEEN

Putting the spark back

You wear yourself out in the pursuit of wealth or love or freedom, you do everything to gain some right – and once it's gained, you take no pleasure in it.

Oriana Fallaci

Women's magazines never shut up about their favourite topic – Putting the Spark Back. They give the impression that if you've been with a partner for over six months, your sex life's automatically on the wane, and you need to devote hours nightly to prancing about with a feather boa, reminding each other that you have genitals. The brutal truth is, everyone's sex life wanes after a while. Show me someone who's having hot, daily sex after five years in a relationship, and I'll show you someone who's just begun an affair. Most big relationships start off in a flurry of lust – new couples say, 'We won't be like everyone else, will we?' and 'I can't imagine not wanting to shag you every five minutes', and irritate their friends by climbing all over each other at social gatherings. This is the 'cheap suit' phase of a relationship (as in 'all over each other like a ...') – but it moves on, inevitably, when both parties realize that the frantic drive to procreate has been succeeded somewhat by the frantic drive not to get sacked from work. Life is not meant to be lived only in a bubble of sexual excitement (harsh but true, and, hell, it took me years to realize this) – once you get past the first three to six months, real life intervenes, you start noticing the annoying way your previously perfect partner hisses when he laughs, or yawns like a girl, and suddenly, the idea of a few nights spent watching *Friends* and painting your nails seems a viable alternative to swinging from the lampshade naked.

Further down the line, of course, sex takes a back seat to moving in, work, mortgages, social life, children, and tiredness. If the relationship's good, it's still there, hovering in the background like a mistress at a funeral, but it tends to happen sporadically. The old saying 'If you put a penny in a jar every time you have sex for the first year, and take one out every time you have sex after that, you'll never empty it' is not quite, but almost, true in many cases. So all the stuff you read about how the average couple is at it three times a week and twice on Saturdays is generally pants, and can be entirely ignored – who's going to tell the truth in a survey, for heaven's sake? After a while, sex tends to happen in cycles – going through a tired, or argumentative phase, it doesn't happen much at all; going through a relaxed and generally happy phase, it happens quite a lot. It's also largely true to say that the more you have, the more you want, so if you don't have any for a bit, you're likely to forget quite how good it can be.

One of the reasons so many couples split, sadly, is unrealistic expectations, so if you go into your relationship thinking you'll never feel less sexual than you do at the start, you'll imagine, when your libido naturally levels off, that there's something wrong with the whole thing and that it can never be good again. This is not remotely true: you'll simply run off with the next guy and a year down the line, wonder why you're starting to miss *Friends* so badly, and realize you can't be bothered to squeeze into yet another black lace corset on a Thursday night ... so it pays to attempt to make your sex life with your current partner as good as it can possibly be. Which means making an effort.

what kind of effort?

The trouble is, everyone assumes that sex is this mystical event that just 'happens' and that to plan it too much in advance, or acknowledge that it could do with being a bit better, is virtually an admittance that it's all over and you may as well wear stripy pyjamas to bed and read gardening books before you turn the light out. This is not the case at all – everything good takes effort after a while. When you were 18 you may have looked naturally gorgeous after six pints and no sleep, but by 28 you're spending a fortune on ceramide-enhanced moisturisers and leg waxes just to get through the day.

And it's the same with sex. If you don't make the effort it will go off the boil, inevitably – and neither of you can simply sit back and expect it to happen without any help whatsoever. For a start, remind yourself that not being in the mood doesn't mean you can't get into the mood. How many times have you almost not bothered to go to a party, or met a friend, because you didn't feel like it – then, when you forced yourself, and got there, you had a great time? Well, trust me, it's the same with sex.

planning it

Time is a major factor in your sex-drought. You may vaguely hope you'll have sex this week – but Monday you worked late and were knackered, Tuesday he went out with his old mates, Wednesday you had friends round and didn't get to bed until one, Thursday you fell asleep in front of the TV, Friday you went for drinks after work and came in pissed ... and somehow, another week's slipped by of you being simply polite bed partners who occasionally throw an arm round each other during sleep. This is when you start getting into dangerous territory, and begin thinking of him as more of a friendly housemate than the man you once couldn't breathe at the sight of. Which is why you need to prioritize sex once again. Perhaps not to the extent you once did, when you didn't go out for three months – but certainly to the point of planning it. Forget spontaneity: it's not working. You don't need to write it on your wall calendar – but you do need to set aside specific time for having sex. You may be the most efficient couple in the world, but this is more important than financial planning, or trips to Ikea – or even, sometimes, seeing your friends. Taking each other for granted is the biggest relationship-killer (second only to 'shagging other people', which can easily become a by-product), so make the effort, or else. Of course, if you discuss the situation and agree 'Right, we'll put the answerphone on, Thursday night, and go to bed,' you may spend all of Thursday in a rage of resentment that you can't come home and watch telly, which is what you feel like doing. You're supposed to look forward to it, so pick a night when you genuinely don't have much else on, and plan it in advance. Change the sheets, buy wine, and consider the sexual excesses you used to enjoy together – then consider trying them again. Of course, you must remember to tell him your arrangements, or he'll ring on his mobile to say he's gone drinking with clients, and you'll be left with clean sheets and no one to put in them.

Ideally, you will both make an effort before you meet – you know how your armpits are harbouring jungle growths, and you've taken to scraping your hair back with a clip and wearing woolly socks whilst watching telly, while he slips on his stained trackie bottoms, and absentmindedly bites his hangnails off? That's all terribly intimate, but at least try and pretend that you still want to impress each other. Showers, shaves, make-up in your case, (aftershave in his) – and if you really mean it, wear stockings. It's bound to feel a little awkward at first – particularly if you climb into bed at 7 p.m., and lie there side by side, sighing and saying, 'Right, so, shall we get on with it then?'

But if you crack open the wine first, have a bit of a snog, and then head for bed, you should soon remember exactly what you're doing there. It's like riding a bike, honestly. Especially if you're very bony, ho, ho ...

communication

The biggest chance you have of relighting each other's gently glowing fires is to recall the hackneyed old advice about relationships trotted out by everyone from thrice-married aunties to Relate counsellors. Which is, nonetheless, valid – because it's all about communication. If you've stopped telling each other what you want sexually – or perhaps you never started – it's no wonder things aren't quite as hot and heavy as you'd like. More tepid and lightweight. Because if you don't talk about what turns you on, how is anyone, least of all your partner, going to know? You get into a routine very quickly – 'push this, twiddle here, seems to work' – and the whole process of turning each other on becomes as efficient as turning on a stereo. You know what button does what, so you're hardly going to bother rewiring the whole thing to see if you can get a slightly different sound, are you? But then again, maybe you should. Because by the law of diminishing returns, the more you do something, the less exciting it gets. And in order to get your sex life up and running again, you really need to take a whole different approach. A handy way to do this is to begin your evening with an honest (and, hopefully, drink-fuelled) conversation. The golden rule, of course, being 'never say anything even vaguely negative about your partner's performance'. Simply take turns to tell each other something that would turn you on – anything from 'having my neck kissed', to 'having a cucumber up the bum' (maybe wait till you're fairly drunk before bringing this one up, however ...), the idea being that you will shortly retire to bed and do these very things. Whatever you do, however, don't begin any of your turn-ons by saying, 'Why do you never ...?' and don't, for a second, think it's acceptable to say, 'I can't really feel your willy when it's inside me', even if this is true. That will not help matters, I swear.

Bear in mind that he will almost certainly be craving new or, at least, different experiences too – so be prepared to put his needs into practice. Actually, I can tell you exactly what his needs will be – summed up by those two little words, 'more blowjobs'. But, while you may be rolling your eyes at the very idea of having to mess up your hair, and gag and generally get an achey jaw, bear in mind that you used to do it happily – and sometimes you aren't just doing these things to get sexual kicks, you're doing them to show you love each other. Kicks are just a bonus.

Keep talking when in bed, too – and not about work stress. Muttering '... and she says she's going to kill me if I don't get those reports finished' when he's licking your thigh is not even vaguely conducive to passion. But whispering 'That feels so nice' and 'You're so sexy', and all those things that you used to bother to say, is.

what to do

Of course, rekindling can seem like hard work. Perhaps you simply can't be bothered to gussy yourself up in fancy knickers, and retire to bed early. In which case, you need a charge of dynamite under your sex life, not merely a light kick up the arse. Which is when you're going to need something special – and what could be more special, as the adverts say, than a night (or, better still, a weekend) in a nice hotel?

Don't give me that 'can't afford it' nonsense – you don't need to go to Barcelona, you can check into the tavern down the road if you want. Scour the Internet for good deals (*late-rooms.co.uk* is very good if you've left it late – because the later you leave it, the cheaper rooms get). And if you're wondering why you'd be bothering to pack all your stuff and drive two miles across town for one night with a minibar and a trouser press, here's the reason: because sometimes you simply need a change of environment. Doing it once again in your bedroom with the overflowing laundry basket, and the alarm clock set for work, and the same old sheets on the same old bed ... it's just not that exciting, is it? Sometimes you don't want to eat in, so you go to a restaurant – and sometimes you don't want to have sex in, so you go to a hotel. And if you really can't afford it, bribe a friend with a nicer house to let you stay one night when she's away.

Hotels are best, however, because they offer total anonymity. You could be anyone checking in, they don't care – so look at it as leaving your personal history at the door, and spending a night of passion without reliving all the other nights of telly and arguing you've had since you met. You are almost certain to feel less inhibited than you do at home, because the normal distractions aren't there – you can just concentrate on each other's bodies, rather than each other's petty grievances.

But a word of warning – don't go for a big romantic meal first. It's guaranteed you'll fall asleep five minutes after you arrive back in the room.

games

Now, if you're still not convinced, you may need both a charge of dynamite AND a man in a hard yellow hat plunging down the handle to set it off. Which is why you might want to consider playing some games. Not 'Thank God, we can forget about all that messy business and have a nice round of Scrabble' games, silly – sex games. They're perfect for ridding you of your inhibitions, and making a sex life which has become a bit of a chore seem the best fun you can have with your clothes off. And there are all kinds to choose from ...

THE DICE GAME

There are several variations on this theme – you can buy 'love dice' which come in pairs – one die has body parts on, the other has instructions like 'tickle' and 'kiss'. But personally, I'd recommend making up your own, because otherwise you run the risk of having 'tickle feet' pop up three times in a row, and it can get dull. So write six parts, six things to do: suggestions are 'clitoris/penis, nipples, bum, chest, mouth, neck'; and six things to do to them – 'kiss, lick, stroke, nibble, suck and blow' are useful. Though he will keep attempting to weight the dice so he gets 'blow penis'.

Alternatively, write six sexual positions and six locations – for example, 'doggy, missionary, standing, sitting, girl on top, legs on shoulders' and 'kitchen, shower, garden, living room, car, stairs'. Then hope to God you don't throw 'stairs, legs on shoulders'. The point of the game is, whatever the dice say, you have to do – there can be no argument once they have spoken. And the chances are, you won't have time to argue as you manoeuvre yourself into 'standing, in the car.' You watch you don't put your backs out, that's all.

STRIP POKER, TRIVIAL PURSUIT, SNAKES AND LADDERS

Start off fully clothed. Play as normal, except when you go up a ladder, or lose a hand, or get a question wrong, you can instruct him which item of his clothing he must remove. When you go down a snake, though, he instructs you. If you like, you can put something back on whenever he has to take something off. The winner is the first person to finish the game with some clothes left on – if you get that far, obviously. The temptation is to try and lose, of course – but ultimately it's a win–win situation.

FORFEITS

You can do it with playing cards (21 is good, being simple yet effective), betting games, or even tiddlywinks. But whenever you lose, the other player demands a sexual forfeit. Start small – a kiss on the cheek, say – and work your way up, so by the time they've nearly lost all their cards, they're stark naked, and you're doing a handstand whilst attempting to perform oral sex. Just don't fall over. For this to work, you need confidence, alcohol, and an ability to forget everything you did by the next morning. With them, it's brilliant. Without, it'll haunt you for years.

NAKED HIDE AND SEEK

Switch all the lights out, so the house is pitch-dark. Take your clothes off. Then, one of you hides, the other seeks – but you do it by touch. When you find each other, do whatever you feel like to celebrate. The only problem is, it can all too easily end up like the very scary bit in *Silence of the Lambs*, where you're edging round the house, holding your arms over your chest like Babs Windsor in *Carry on Camping*, and leaping 10 feet in the air with terror every time you hear a little rustle. So you must make him promise that if you get The Fear, and ask where he is, he has to tell you, not go spookily silent. It's meant to be sexy, not petrifying.

TONIGHT MATTHEW, I'M GOING TO BE ...

This is sex in the style of a famous person. Or, better still, someone you know. It's simple – you get in bed, start proceedings – (kissing and foreplay counts too), but you have to do it as you imagine your chosen celebrity would. Talking is allowed. And when your imitation is correctly guessed, swap turns. Suggestions include Sharon Stone (be wildly over-confident, mention ice picks) and, for him, Liam Gallagher (be rough, graceless and vaguely sexy), or a *Blue Peter* presenter (pretend to make a spaceship out of his willy) and – well, the possibilities are endless, really. But it rids you of inhibitions once again – because you're acting a role, albeit during sex.

Of course, you can play any damn sex game you like – these are simply to kick off with. And if you're still bored after that, I have to say it may be time to worry. Because if, whatever you do, that old spark is failing to ignite like a dodgy boiler, it may be time to take a close look at what's going on in your relationship ...

what if it won't rekindle?

Bad news. You've tried everything, done the whole, 'champagne–hotel–giant vibrators' scenario ... and still your sex life's slightly less exciting than watching *The Bill* with only a boiled egg for tea? It's time to face the fact, then, that you have simply stopped fancying him. Simple as that. He may still fancy the pants off you – he may be desperate to get in your knickers on a regular basis – but if your drive's gone, it's gone. Don't confuse this with tiredness, illness, stress or argument-induced lack of sex drive – all these factors can put a massive vacuum where your sexual desire used to be situated. But these are temporary factors. They can be overcome, once you get better, or the workload eases off, or you go on holiday. It's when it doesn't even flicker for months, when you're getting on fine, there's no new perceptible stresses in your life, and no reason not to enjoy a nice roll around together, that it's indicative of something not quite right. Basically, it points to the fact that you've stopped fancying him, and that it may be time to move on.

fancying others

Ceasing to fancy your partner is obviously not good news for the relationship. However, fancying other people whilst still fancying your own man is not the disaster it initially appears. It is highly likely, in fact, that over the course of your relationship you will fancy several other people. So, you're a little bored of life with your bloke. Your sex life isn't great right now. Some little charmer comes along, looks good, pays you a few compliments ... and of course you're going to fancy him. But just remember: there's a massive difference between fancying, and actually doing anything about it. Fancying = fun, minor thrill, makes you feel alive. Doing something about it = hideous guilt, utter embarrassment, and the end of your relationship when your bloke finds out, which he almost certainly will. So accept that, while your eye may wander from time to time, it had better remain your eye, and not your hands. And try every trick in the book; this one, to be specific: to improve your sex life with the guy you have, not the one you fancy from afar.

And finally, two essential tips for spark-relighting.

how to give a massage

BACK MASSAGE

Don't press too hard. Keep up a steady pressure, making firm movements towards the heart. Make the same movement with each hand, at the same speed and pressure. Start right at the base of the spine – initially, you need to heat up the muscles and get the blood supply circulating. Use light pressure, up over the top of the shoulders and under the armpits. Then concentrate on the spine, because most people have tensions around that area. Move up with finger rotations, being careful not to press on the spine itself, then gently move back and start again. Always work upwards. It's easier to group your three fingers together than use the whole hand, so that when you rotate them it takes pressure off your wrists.

If he has tense muscles around his shoulder blades, get him to put his arms behind his back, and rest it just at the base of his spine – that allows you to get under it.

You can use scented oil, a base oil, or baby oil – anything that'll act as a lubricant so the skin doesn't drag. Take half an hour over it – then you can massage anywhere else you like. But make sure you're in a warm environment, because being cold isn't remotely relaxing.

HOW TO STRIP LIKE A PRO

Most men would die for the chance to see their girlfriend strip. So why not make his year by giving it a go? Choose music carefully – nothing too fast, as it's got to be slow and erotic. But make sure it's got a good beat – Madonna or Prince works well.

Clothing is very important. Wear a top and short skirt that zip undone, elbow-length gloves, lace-top hold-up stockings, and high heels.

Take your top off first, but zip and unzip it halfway a couple of times, to tease him.

Never wear a top you have to pull over your head: it ruins the whole effect when you emerge red-faced with hair like a nest. Remove it one arm at a time, and toss it aside. Stopping to fold your clothes, however neat you normally are, is not advisable stripper behaviour.

Stand with your back to him, bend over, slowly unzip your skirt and kick it aside. Turn round again, put your hands on your hips and grind them lightly.

Slip one strap off your shoulders, then the other – turn so your back's to him again, and remove the bra or basque.

When you turn around, put your hands over your breasts to conceal them.

You tease. At some point, though, you need to let them show. Slowly move one hand, then the other.

Slip your hands under the straps of your knickers and pull them up, then push them down a little way.

A G-string is preferable to knickers at this stage – it'll make you feel more like a real stripper, and gives that almost-but-not-quite naked look.

Turn away and, keeping your legs together, drop the knickers, straight to your ankles.

Make sure your legs are straight and bend forward slightly as you push them down. Step neatly aside, feet back together, and spin round to face him, wearing only stockings and high heels.

It's best to leave your shoes and stockings on – there's no good time to take them off, and bare feet are far less seductive than stilettos.

Now he can touch you.

CHAPTER FOURTEEN

Contraception

There is nothing safe about sex. There never will be.

Norman Mailer

The whole point of sex, as far as nature's concerned, is to make babies. If you want to have sex without the pregnancy bit, then you're going to have to make sure that your chosen contraception runs more smoothly than a German car driven by an Italian gigolo. Sadly, given that nature is a fairly powerful force, when confronted with our weedy attempts to stop her planet-populating progress, most contraception fails to be 100 per cent effective – and if you don't use it properly, my dears, it fails to be at all effective. Given that sex is geared towards getting carried away on a tide of passion, however, it's likely that at least once – and possibly even several times – in your life, you will mess up by failing to use it properly. Everybody does. So, to avoid mishaps – the sort of mishaps that are going to result in you never getting a wink of sleep for the next 18 years, that is – you might want to take your baby-prevention measures seriously. You have to rise above the temptation to throw yourself at the feet of passion, and sigh 'Don't make me think of mundanities, I want you to take me now ...' and in fact say, 'I want you to take me now, but wait just a moment while I deal with my yearning ovaries.' Of course, if you're in a long-term relationship, there are several options that mean you don't have to think about ruining the moment. If you're not, you have to use a condom. And, given that it's the only method of contraception that men have to be responsible for, you might as well make him use one anyway – because you're stuck with sorting out pretty much everything else.

the combined pill

As the poet said, 'Sexual intercourse began in 1963,' the year the pill was invented. It did spark a sexual revolution – no doubt about it, even though the idea of your mother indulging in Free Love in her shagadelic mini-dress is probably not an image you want to conjure with for long. However, since its early days, when the hormone doses were so high women felt sick all month, and suffered migraines from the amount of oestrogen flooding their systems, it's come a long way, baby. There are enough different brands on the market to try various types if one doesn't suit you – but all of them work the same way, by preventing the release of the monthly egg from your ovaries, by mimicking the hormones of pregnancy, thus fooling your body into thinking it's already pregnant. Though, of course, you don't get the chocolate cravings, and nobody stands up for you on buses. It also thickens the mucus from your cervix, which makes it difficult for sperm to burst through it and reach an egg, and makes the lining of your womb thinner so it can't accept a fertilized egg.

The combined pill is over 99 per cent effective if you follow the instructions – and let's face it, you'd have to be slightly dim not to, as the pills come in little capsules with your days of the week marked on them. The only drawback is, if you have a sieve-like memory, it's guaranteed you'll forget now and then, and throw yourself into a huge panic. Also, sickness and diarrhoea can disrupt the pills' effectiveness – so if you have a habit of going out and getting slaughtered, best not put your faith in the pill.

Its advantages are, reduction of PMT (winner!), heavy bleeding, and period pain, and it can protect against cancer of the ovary and the womb. The downsides, however, are the possible side effects. You may still suffer nausea if you're on a high-dose brand, and headaches are common. And weight gain, tender breasts, and mood changes. Nice. There are more rare but serious side effects – in fact, to read the warning leaflet, you'd think they'd just done a round-up of intensive-care ailments – but the main ones you need to know about are blood clots, breast and cervical cancer; the risk only increases marginally, but increase it does. Nor does the combined pill protect against sexually transmitted diseases. There's also the fact that a tiny number of users have developed blood clots – risks are greatest if you're very overweight, immobile, or a member of your family has suffered one. But, apart from that, you go, girls. Basically, it's best for those who are young, healthy, in a long-term relationship, who want to put off having kids for a while. When you do want them, in theory, you can get pregnant as soon as you come off the pill. But you really do have to remember to take it.

the progesterone-only pill

Also 99 per cent effective, 'if taken according to instructions'. (What else are you going to do: throw them all in the air, shouting 'Wheee!' and wonder why you got pregnant?) The basic difference is that the lack of oestrogen means you have fewer hormones flooding your body – the mini-pill, as it's known, works by thickening the plug of mucus at the entrance to your vagina – look, I never said this was pleasant – and preventing the sperm from reaching the egg. It is less invasive that the pill itself, but you do have to remember to take it at the same time each day – so it really isn't a choice suitable for forgetful girls, on any level. Or, in fact, anyone with an irregular lifestyle.

Unfortunately, rather than being the marvellous period regulator that is the combined pill, this one can cause them to go all irregular, with a bit of bleeding in between. And, of course, it is no protection against sexually transmitted diseases (STDs) either. It's handy, though, if you're efficient, have a great memory, are in a long-term relationship, and don't like the hormone frenzy of the combined pill.

the morning after pill

Can be used up to 72 hours after you've had sex where a) you were drunk, b) the condom broke, and c) you were drunk, but you're telling the nurse the condom broke. They're basically high-dose combined pills, taken 12 hours apart – and because the doses are so massive they're not good for you. If you're thinking of relying on them as handy daft-bird contraception, forget it – they carry a risk of blood clots, strokes, faintness and, without question, major nausea. It's entirely likely you'll sick them up – but if so, you'll simply have to take more, and live with the waves of sickness. And does he get away with his night of unprotected fun? You guessed it. Still, better 12 hours of feeling appalling than nine months, eh? Just don't make a habit of it.

injectable contraception

Again, this is a winner in the effectiveness stakes, being over 99 per cent effective. The contraceptive injection is a large dose of progestogen, injected into your bum – it can last for 12 weeks (Depo-Provera) or eight weeks (Noristerat). It's injected into muscle and works in the same way as the pill, so if you really want a form of contraception that you can forget about for three months – say, you're going on a lap-dancing tour of Nevada, with only room to pack a toothbrush and a G-string – it may be ideal. However, for many women it isn't – not because it isn't convenient, but simply because the side effects can make what happened to the Incredible Hulk look like a minor reaction to antibiotics.

There are even support groups for women who suffered reactions long after the contraceptive wore off – and, the trouble is, once it's in your bloodstream, it ain't going to go away for a good long while, so if it doesn't suit you, there's nothing you can do about it. Some women have gained excessive weight, or suffered severe migraines, major mood swings, acne, bloating and depression. Basically, you may become Kathy Bates in *Misery* overnight. Periods can also become irregular, or stop altogether – which may, obviously, be a good thing. However, unless you have a really good reason for wanting to be free of contraception worries, think carefully about potential problems, and talk the options through with your clinic first.

implants

Basically work the same way as injections – it's a small, flexible tube, or tubes, which you have implanted under the skin of your arm, that releases progestogen over five years. You can now only have Implanon, as the alternative (Norplant) was banned from future use in 1999, but more are due on the market. Despite conjuring visions of futuristic ID-tagging, it is immensely convenient if you want a contraceptive device that can work unaided for up to three years. It's also more than 99 per cent effective, and works, again, like the pill. But, it's not that attractive a thought to have rods stuck inside your arm – and unless you have a very good reason, it may be hard to get them removed. Pretty good reasons, however, may include such side effects as acne, mood changes, depression, headaches and breast tenderness – all the misery of being a teenager, but none of the fun. It may also cause irregular periods, with some missed ones, or irregular bleeding in between. And it certainly won't protect you against STDs. So if you're going to risk it, make sure you know all the facts first, because it won't be much fun if you start feeling like an alien force is taking over your body but can't get the damn thing removed for months – because it has to be removed by a specially trained doctor, and is harder to remove than to put in, so it's not a short-term solution.

IUD/IUS

The intra-uterine device is more usually fitted when you've had children, and is placed at the entrance to your womb. Are you beginning to suspect that all is not fair in the world of contraception? That men, in fact, get away scot-free? Yep, don't worry. You're absolutely right. They don't get their intimate bits interfered with, they can simply sprinkle their sperm wherever it suits them. But we're getting off the point here.

The IUD, then, is a small plastic and copper device that looks like an elf's bottle opener, with a thread coming out of the end, and hangs in your vagina. They can stay in for between three and 10 years, and have to be fitted by a trained doctor or nurse (and you thought you'd pick one up at the elf off-licence, eh?). They're claimed to be 98 per cent effective, but there are many stories of babies arriving, waving the IUD aloft, so don't count on it. It supposedly stops the sperm reaching the egg, and works immediately it's implanted. So you don't know it's there, and it means you can shag away without worrying. Or it does in theory. The down-sides, however, are so far down you're practically potholing. You may suffer painful, heavy, longer periods. Great. You may get an infection during the first three weeks – and if you have more than one partner (over 10 years? well, I guess you might), you could get a pelvic infection at any point. Lovely. It can be pushed out by your womb, or shift inside you – so you've got to check your threads, OK? Now here's where it gets real nice: occasionally, an IUD can perforate your cervix when fitted, and guess what, you might not even know about it, because it doesn't always hurt. Oh, hurrah. Then, if you do get pregnant, you may have an ectopic pregnancy, where the baby develops outside the womb, which is very dangerous. Oh, and of course there's no protection against STDs. So, sound like the contraception for you? Well, it works for some women. Apparently.

The IUS looks similar, but works by thickening your cervical mucus, and thinning the lining of your uterus. It works for five years, and unlike the IUD it makes your periods lighter, shorter and less painful. But you may suffer headaches, acne, tenderness of breasts ... the usual suspects, then. Like the IUD, it can be pushed out, or move – basically, the problems are similar, but if you have heavy, painful periods it's worth considering.

male condoms

Presumably you know how condoms work. If you were around in the 1980s, you can barely have missed earnest agony-aunt types pinging them over cucumbers at every televisual opportunity, and endless government leaflets explaining exactly how to interrupt your lovemaking in order to put one on. What could be sexier? Unfortunately, most men are still convinced that having sex wearing a condom is like having a shower in a thick raincoat. And indeed, often condoms do dull sensitivity, for both of you, by turning a nice, warm, lively penis into a chilly, sheathed, bullet-like object. But that's irrelevant. Because the bottom line is, **You Have To Use One**. Unless you've been with the guy long enough to know every single in and out of his sexual history, and have committed yourself to another, failsafe form of contraception, read my lips: **You Have No Choice**. Because if the guy is not the love of your life a) one little slip and possibly you're a single mother, and b) one little slip and you're possibly suffering from some obnoxious disease that he picked up from a prostitute in Amsterdam. Or AIDS.

So, however unpleasant it seems to whisk one out of your bedside drawer – or handbag, or bra – you're just going to have to get over it. It's like public speaking – once you've done it the first time, it gets a whole lot easier the next time.

Needless to say, it'd be nice if he was enough of a gent to sort out the contraceptive side of things himself – but then, not all men assume they're going to get lucky. And a few hope you'll say, 'Ha ha, what do we need a condom for? Nasty little things,' before straddling him with a carefree laugh. Unlikely, but they can dream. Forget all that last-century nonsense about 'Ooh, what will he think of me if he knows I was expecting to have sex?' A darn sight more than he will when you ring him three weeks later, and quiver, 'Remember me? I've got something to tell you ...' down his mobile. So Have Condoms Handy, and **Use Them**. The right moment to put one on is when his willy is waving free in the breeze, but as yet it's nowhere near your bits. You know you're going to have sex, as does he, and after a bit of oral or hand manipulation, now's your chance. Watching you walk across the room naked to get them should not diminish his ardour one jot. You can either delicately hand it to him to roll on – but sometimes, in their excitement, men fail to do this properly, vaguely apply the thing to their penis like a bumbling idiot, and then wonder how on earth it came off inside you. So maybe you should do it yourself.

THE CORRECT WAY TO PUT ON A CONDOM

The male condom is 98 per cent effective if used correctly. Wait till he has a full erection. Obvious, I know, but you'd be surprised. Tear open the packet, keeping any long fingernails and scratchy rings out of the way. Squeeze the closed end – and make sure you've got it the right way up. If you have, the edges are rolled upwards. Place your fingers, still holding the top, against the end of his willy, and push it down over it till it reaches the base. And when he's come, he should pull out right away, before his erection has a chance to subside, holding the base of his willy, and pull it off well away from your bits. Then he simply has to tie a knot in the end and chuck it away – not down the toilet, (it'll get blocked, and you don't want to be the person who has to explain it all to the plumber).

It can go wrong. If he doesn't come out of you quickly enough, semen can leak. Or if he touches his willy then your vagina, he can transfer sperm. Or if you don't squeeze the air out of the end – then, thrusting can make it burst. And finally, if you use oil-based lubricants, like Vaseline, they can rot the rubber (or polyurethane, to give it its correct term), so it's KY or nothing, I'm afraid.

Condoms have improved dramatically since gentlemen were forced to wrap their manhoods in bits of sheepskin. You can get such a huge variety that you can easily avoid the sensation of a thick rubber coating – try Avanti from Durex, which are fantastically thin and allow body heat through. Well, if you want, you can try a luminous yellow one with a sheep's head on the end. But it may not be very sexy. Forget flavoured condoms, as they all taste of synthetic sweeties, whatever they claim – and glow-in-the-dark ones are really only suitable for stag-night pranks. Except if you're the stripper.

the female condom

Unsurprisingly, the female condom (or Femidom) has failed to take the world by storm. Launched with tons of fanfare, it is not most women's contraceptive of choice – but it does suit some, so here goes. It's 95 per cent effective. (But do you feel you can afford that five per cent chance? OK, it's your lookout.)

The bonus is you can put it in any time before sex – but well before his penis touches your bits. And, because you're going to be fiddling around with your bits, you should get into the position that suits you when inserting tampons – standing, one leg up, or lying down (then again, who inserts tampons lying down?). Then, get it (carefully) out of the packet. Hold the closed end, and squeeze the inner ring between your finger and thumb. Separate your labia. Hopefully, this will look sexier than it sounds, if he happens to be watching this little interlude. Put the squeezed ring inside your vagina and push it up as high as you can. Put your finger inside the open end, till you can feel the inner ring, then push it as far back as it will go, so it's lying just above your pubic bone. The outer ring should be pressed against the entrance to your vagina. It's normal for it to move about during sex – but as long as you make sure his willy's actually inside the condom, not cosily lying next to it, you'll be OK. To get it out afterwards, twist the outer ring, pull it out, and chuck it away.

You begin to see why it's not the most popular option, don't you? It's just a bit of a faff. Then again, it's easy once it's in, and it doesn't have to interrupt the moment like the male condom does. Not unless you call his penis rustling around as if it's in a giant crisp bag 'interrupting the moment', at any rate.

the rhythm method (or natural family planning)

This used to be a highly popular method – and still is for Catholics. Based on the fact that there are only a few days in every month you can get pregnant, NFP teaches you to recognize when you're ovulating, and avoid sex on those days. It's fairly effective once you know what you're doing – if you don't, it's about as much use as wearing a condom on your head. It's also a huge pain in the arse. But if you can't use contraception for reasons of side effects, a 'my body is a temple' non-interventionist policy, or religion – or, hell, you just feel like playing pregnancy Russian roulette for a while – it's worth learning.

I'm not going to be responsible for teaching you, though – you think I want to be held to blame when you've just had twins because you counted wrong? However, the basics are as follows.

The natural method works by recording your menstrual cycle, every day. You take your temperature when you wake up, check your cervical mucus (mmm, who needs breakfast?) and observe how long your periods last. You can get pregnant for about nine days of each month, maximum. So that gives you three weeks of stress-free sex. Kind of. Although the egg only lives for a day, sperm can wait around for up to a week, like groupies hanging around the stage door – so there's still a chance one might get an autograph. I think that extends that metaphor far enough ...

If you use it properly, NFP can be 98 per cent effective. The good points are, there are no fake hormones whizzing around or weird devices stuck up you. The bad news is, to learn properly it takes three to six months, and you need to keep daily records, no matter how hungover or busy you are. Also, if you get ill or stressed, it can confuse your cycle – and, therefore, you. You both have to be committed – this ain't one for one-night stands. And, needless to say, there are nine days when you absolutely have to use condoms, or else the whole tiresome exercise becomes rather pointless.

So, you need a fertility thermometer, and a chart – the fertile period ends when you have three days in a row when your temperature's higher than the previous six days. In fact, it helps if you passed Maths GCSE (I didn't). The difference will be a minuscule 0.4°F – like I say, you've really got to learn this properly. You also need to keep a beady eye on your cervical secretions. Delightful. When it's like raw egg white, you're at your most fertile. But you need to master both methods before you can be sure.

Alternatively, a far simpler method is Persona, which costs around £50 for the basic kit and £10 a month for the test sticks thereafter. The unit, which looks like a glasses case, has a display screen, which tells you whether you're fertile or not, after you wee on a stick and insert it into the unit. It's all very neat and efficient – and you have to do it nearly every day for the first few months, then less as it becomes familiar with your cycle. But if you forget one day, it messes the whole thing up, and you're back to square one. It is, however, a whole lot simpler than the really natural natural method.

cap/diaphragm

The rather worrying 92–96 per cent success rating offered by the cap suggests it's one for the woman whose life would not fall apart if she did happen to get pregnant. These are, however, non-hormonal, handy little devices and worth bearing mind for that reason. All they do is stop sperm reaching the egg by fitting over your cervix, and because you use them in conjunction with spermicide any sperm that did make it would soon be dead. It's a cruel business, I grant you.

You have to put it in less than three hours before you have sex – but that's OK, who the hell's that confident? If you do, you have to remember to use extra spermicide. Then you have to leave it for six hours afterwards. There are various sizes and shapes of the things – you have to be fitted for it, though, and the doctor can guide you through the options. It's more interesting than the usual GP's chat about your persistent cough, mind you.

The downsides are, it can interrupt sex if you didn't know you were going to be having it, and therefore turned up unprepared. You have to spend time learning how to put it in properly – and if you aren't 100 per cent friendly with your own genitals, it can be a bit stressful as it boings round the room, covered with spermicide. Also, diaphragms can encourage cystitis, as they can irritate the vaginal walls.

To put one in, you need to put two strips of spermicide on either side, then squeeze it, with your finger in the middle. Slide it in downwards and backwards, and check you can feel your cervix under the rubber. If not – hey, start again! He can always read your diary or think about football while he waits. For the cap, fill a third with spermicide, but not round the rim. Squeeze the sides together, and slide in. Add some more spermicide – and away you go. Six short hours later, hook it out, rinse it, and keep it in a clean, dry place till next time. No, not the bottom of your handbag, you old tart.

CHAPTER FIFTEEN

Nasty diseases

There are no good girls gone wrong, just bad girls found out.

Mae West

There are no truly obvious downsides to sex, at first glance. It feels nice, it's fun, it gives you something to think about during the boring bits at work. Oh yes, and it brings you and your partner to new levels of joy and oneness, of course. But – and there's always a but – there is one downside. And it's rather more significant than the 'Oh my God, he had ginger pubes and his ears stuck out' morning-after horror. We're talking sexually transmitted diseases (STDs). And, worryingly, there are quite a few of the damn things, all of which you can get from sexual contact. Some are minor, and merely irritating because you have to wee all the time. Some are more serious, because they can affect your fertility and, occasionally, even destroy it altogether. And some are deadly, with no cure at all. It's a bit of a price to pay for a daft night of unprotected sex – so it's well worth being aware of the causes, the symptoms, and the cures of the various unpleasant diseases that can colonize your intimate bits if you're a bit free with your affections, without being stern about condom usage. I know, it's all getting very serious, but I've been racking my brains for a herpes joke, and I just can't come up with one. So, instead, here's the list – but don't go reading it and imagining you've got every single one. The chances are you're perfectly fine, and just wearing itchy knickers. But if you do suspect you've got any of them, run like the wind to your nearest clinic – they won't be judgmental, it's what they exist for – and tell them. Then, unfortunately, you'd better tell the guy you slept with last night. Oops ...

what are the signs of an STD?

Sometimes there aren't any symptoms – which is, as you can imagine, rather unhelpful when it comes to diagnosis. Sometimes he'll have symptoms and you won't – or vice versa. But you may be alerted by discharge of an unusual nature, pain or a burning sensation when you wee, any itching, rash, lumps or blisters around your bits and, particularly, pain or bleeding after you've had sex. But the good news is, if you catch them early, most can be cured fairly painlessly. So don't sit around itching for three weeks because you're too embarrassed to go to the clinic. Besides, they're very common, which isn't actually great, but at least it means you're not on your own.

chlamydia

Over half of infected people have no symptoms at all – which isn't as good as it sounds, because you really don't want it to get a hold while you're blithely going about your business, sleeping with all and sundry. The bacteria affects your cervix (and men's urethra) and visible symptoms include yellow vaginal discharge, bleeding between periods, and pain when you wee – he gets away more lightly, with mere discharge and pain on weeing. The bad news is, if you don't catch it early, it can lead to pelvic inflammatory disease, which causes lower stomach pain, temperature and discharge, and can damage your fertility. You must go and be tested – they'll take a swab, and it'll take around five days to get the results. But don't think 'Stuff it, I may as well have unprotected sex while I wait,' will you? You'll have caught it through full intercourse with an infected bloke – and it's depressingly easily transmitted. But, hurrah, it's easily blasted away with antibiotics – the really bad news is, you really need to tell whoever you've had sex with, because they need to get treated. And if that list is 'my boyfriend', and 'his brother' then I'm sorry, but that's the price you pay for messing with your Mojo, love.

NSU

Non-specific urethritis is simply inflammation of the urethra – your wee-tube – so it'll burn or sting when you wee. It may not be an infection – then again, a lot go hand in hand (or at least, hand in ... yes, well, you get my point) with inflammation. Again, the doctor will take a swab, but you'll probably be given antibiotics anyway, just in case.

It isn't necessarily sexually transmitted – it can be caused by tight jeans (so all you Bon Jovi fans, take care, now) or overenthusiastic sex, so you're a little bruised. If that's the case, of course, you won't pass it on, but if it's chlamydia masquerading as NSU, then there's every chance you might – so, get it checked. And, really, tight jeans are so over.

warts

Another tasty treat – genital warts. You should know that they're extremely common, so don't fall apart with despair should you break out in a few of the things. They're caused by the human papilloma virus, which has various types – and, fact fans, it's types 6 and 11 that cause warts on the outer genitals, while other types affect the cervix, and can lead to cervical cancer if untreated. But we won't list all those numbers, it's already getting like a wart rugby team.

Genital warts are pretty easy to spot, being cauliflower-like growths, that can grow up to a centimetre across. In fact, you're unlikely to miss them, really. And, once again, the clinic calls. And if the doc's seen one too many cauliflower-shaped things that day, and is feeling a little confused, a solution will be dabbed on, which will stain the warts white if they are of the STD type.

You caught them through sexual contact with infected skin – oral sex is a less likely culprit. Most of us are exposed to the virus at one time or another – but only 10 per cent develop the warts themselves. Also, it can take up to two years for them to flower – so it's often impossible to say when you got them. Not to mention the fact that your loving partner may have contracted them long before you met, but you won't know till they appear like the Demon King in a panto.

They can be treated – but it works best when you can see them. If you've just got the virus, it's more difficult, and they can recur, but not indefinitely. They can be frozen off, using liquid nitrogen, which is all a bit Bond villain, and can be slightly painful – but it does get rid of them. Or they can be treated with Podophyllin, a plant extract that's applied and washed off – but it can be somewhat corrosive. There are also various creams – and for really severe cases, a wart-burning electric current. It's OK, uncross your legs, as this is for extreme cases only.

Needless to say, if either of you has warts, you must use a condom, for handjobs as well. I'd say you'd probably be OK with oral sex – but it's not a terribly appealing thought, is it?

herpes (simplex)

This is the same virus that causes cold sores, but, while a dab of Blistex tends to sort the mouth kind, the genital sort can be painful, unsightly and thoroughly upsetting. The charming truth is that you'll get painful little blisters on your bits, which then burst, and leave ulcers, which then form a crust and finally disappear after about a week. But then, they can come back again, like

Terminator. Basically the virus is concealed in the nerve (which enters via broken or damaged skin) away from the immune system, and it multiplies, and pops out again – and, being nerve-based, it's also hideously sore, often with a tingling feeling just before a break-out. You will, of course, be hotfooting it to the clinic without fail – whereupon, the doctor will look at your weeping sores, mutter, 'Uh-huh, yep, herpes,' then take a swab anyway, just in case. It can take from a few days to a week for definite results.

You can get herpes from a carrier in various ways – oral sex, full sex, even kissing gives cold sores. But you're much more likely to catch it during the middle of an outbreak – in which case, what are you doing having sex with them? Did you not notice their ulcer-riddled genitals? Obviously not ... Also, the infection can hang around for quite some time before popping up – so don't assume your newish bloke's been sleeping around. He may just be the unfortunate victim of dormant herpes. Anyway, here comes the truly bad news. Brace yourself. There's no actual cure. After the first bout, it'll probably recur within six months, but after that it can lie dormant for months or years. There are treatments which can reduce the impact of the attacks – but after the initial medieval torture, most attacks tend to be brief and very mild. So as long as you don't have sex during that time, you should be OK without treatment. You are wildly infectious, though – but that doesn't mean that in between you can't have sex. It just means, **Use A Condom**. And try not to bring it up on a first date.

thrush

Not strictly an STD, because you can develop it whether or not you've had sex. However, it can be passed on via intercourse, so for our purposes let's say it counts. It's basically a fungus, candida, that grows anywhere on the body, but when it gets a hold over your natural bacteria, it causes symptoms – itching and soreness round your bits, and a discharge like ... well, I hope you're not eating any while you read this, but cottage cheese. It'll also make weeing painful. To test for it, you have an internal swab, and you'll get the results right away. But don't necessarily start fretting about who you've slept with – it can be caused by tight clothes, sweating too much, scented bubble bath, or antibiotics. So if you're a heavy metal fan, who frequents overheated dance clubs, has just received a perfumed bath set and is recovering from a persistent cough with a course of Amoxycillin, you're staring trouble in the face thrush-wise. You can tackle it yourself with Canesten cream, or a natural-yoghurt pessary – but remember not to wear your best knickers that day, won't you?

BV (bacterial vaginosis)

Before you get on the phone to your ex and give him hell, be calm – this isn't strictly an STD, and it's easily dealt with. It's actually caused by a change in the make-up of your vaginal bacteria – not, I'll wager, something you generally give a great deal of thought to. However, while you merrily go about your daily business, the lactobacilli in your vagina are working away (I was going to say 'beavering', but...) creating acidic secretions that help prevent infection. BV is caused when those bacteria become replaced by others, such as *Gardnerella* (Cinderella's green-fingered sister) *Vaginalis*, which produces a whitish discharge that smells of fish. It's not dangerous, and the test can be done while you wait. It normally affects youngish women between 20 and 40, although how it's caused is debatable. Unfamiliar semen, or scented soap or douches, swimming around up there can change the bacterial patterns. So stop using fancy soap, and you may also be required to take antibiotics – then, of course, you'll only have to worry about thrush. Great ...

TV/trich (Trichomonas vaginalis)

Right, brace yourself. This little lovely is slightly more developed than your average bacteria – it has four microscopic legs, and looks a little like a prototype jellyfish. Thank God it's invisible to the naked eye. Revoltingly, women get a green, frothy discharge with a fishy smell, and soreness and burning round the vulva. Not really one to bring up when the casual acquaintance asks, 'How are you?', then. You're tested by swab and, from a GP, results will take a week, though after seven days of that you'd probably have a fair idea that all was not well down there. At a GUM clinic, though, you'll get results right away. It is sexually transmitted, through unprotected sex – though men get away with merely a sore penis and white discharge. Very rarely it can be passed on via shared towels. The treatment is simple anti-biotics – but you need to get your partner(s) treated, too, as it's highly infectious.

gonorrhoea (the clap)

Easier to catch than it is to spell, gonorrhoea's been around for centuries. However, while men get soreness and discharge, women can often be unaware there's anything amiss – or symptoms may resemble chlamydia. The trouble is, it can lead to PID (see below), which can affect your fertility if it goes untreated. Testing in GUM clinics will be immediate, luckily. It's caught by sex – oral, anal or vaginal – and develops quickly, within a few days. Antibiotics, again, will see it off – as long as you deal with it and don't ignore signs of trouble, in you or him. It's highly infectious, too – so, once again, it's a tiresome evening on the phone, calling up all the guys you had unprotected sex with over the last few weeks ... damn.

syphilis

Out of the history books and into your pants ... syphilis has made a resurgence in recent years, and is certainly not confined to 18th-century Parisian prostitutes. Syphilis was probably the most famous STD in the world until AIDS turned up. Neverthe-less, syphilis is still a major contender – because it's the only other STD that can cause death if untreated. It's pretty rare – but it's worth knowing why you shouldn't sleep with anyone who may have been exposed to it. The first outbreak leads to a painless genital ulcer – which then colonizes your bloodstream, and breaks out in other areas of your body. As the immune system attempts to get rid of it, it damages the heart and brain over a period of years. Less than a third of sufferers will end up with destroyed hearts and brains – then again, you wouldn't want to be in that 30 per cent, would you? Diagnosis is usually via a blood test, after you've been exposed to the disease. It's passed on by all kinds of sexual contact – and, in the second stage, even non-sexual contact, such as a social kiss (thanks a bunch, Gran). Luckily, as you are not an 18th-century prostitute, doomed to die hideously, there is now a cure, in the form of antibiotics injected daily into muscle. Yum. Plus follow-up courses. If you do have it, you're going to have to host one big party for your exes – it's serious stuff, and they have to know. Though it's not the greatest excuse for a catch-up call, admittedly.

HIV (human immunodeficiency virus)

I know you know this, but just one more time for luck – HIV is not the same thing as AIDS. It began as 'the gay plague' in the early 1980s – but now, most new infections are amongst heterosexuals. The virus attacks the T-cells that protect your body from viruses and infections, and mutates horribly fast, so effortlessly overpowering any immune defence mechanisms. Which means that passing infections which would normally be ignored can take hold dramatically, and, eventually, lead to AIDS (Acquired Immune Deficiency Syndrome). This can take several years. While diagnosis of HIV – via blood test, and with accompanying counselling and confidential results – is often seen as a death sentence, there are now medications which will often postpone AIDS, and help sufferers have a decent quality of life for up to twenty years.

HIV takes three months to show up on a test – so it's no use panicking the day after. The chances are, after unprotected sex with a hetero guy, who's never injected or been bisexual, you'll be OK (stupid, but OK). But if you've reason to think you're in danger (bi heroin user) you have to decide whether you can live with the results if the test is positive. It's generally spread by unprotected sex, or needle-sharing – not social contact, as the virus dies within 10 seconds outside the body. Treatment is for life, and may involve unpleasant side effects – but new advances are constantly being made. But really, there's only one piece of advice that's absolutely invaluable when it comes to avoiding HIV. USE A CONDOM. Simple as that.

PID (pelvic inflammatory disease)

This is the more sinister relation of your common or garden (erella) STD, because it means the infection has worked its way up the vagina, and entered the cervix, and held a party in your uterus, or tubes. It's generally an unfortunate after-effect of untreated gonorrhoea or chlamydia, and causes stomach pain, temperature, discharge, and sometimes irregular bleeding – also, pain during sex can be a symptom. While this is all unpleasant enough, the real worry is that it can damage your Fallopian tubes, and cause either infertility or an ectopic pregnancy. The more outbreaks you have of PID, the greater your chances of this happening – so you must, must, must go to the clinic if you note any symptoms at all, and they will check for a tender cervix, and take a swab. The risk is increased if you've just had a baby, or an abortion, or use a coil (though the risk is only high up to two weeks after it's inserted). One more time, treatment is by our old friends, antibiotics, though you may need to go to hospital in severe cases. Much better, then, to get yourself checked out at the first sign of trouble – before mild chlamydia turns into something much worse.

crabs and scabies

The very idea of crabs makes everyone itch horribly – so the notion that you have the things setting up home in your pubic hair is enough to make you run, screaming, to the nearest pond, to throw yourself in and drown the little bastards. However, panicking will not make them go away. You caught them through rubbing your furry bits against someone else's crab-ridden furry bits – or simply by sleeping in infested bedclothes. And, while either kind isn't the most welcome visitor to your pants, pubic lice are larger and can occasionally be seen with the naked eye (Oh God! Oh God!). Scabies, however, are very small mites, and can only be detected by small red spots on your skin. Both, however, itch like a itchy train ride to Itchytown. In fact, I'm itching thinking about it.

You'll notice them up to six weeks after exposure – and treatment is in the form of special shampoo. You might, however, itch for up to two weeks after they're all gone – calamine lotion, and thinking about anything but miniature bugs dancing around in your pubes, should help. Naturally, you'll need to tell your partner. Like he isn't beside himself with itching anyway ... Basically, crabs are harmless. But oh, lordy, so unpleasant.

cystitis

Cystitis isn't sexually transmitted – it's simple inflammation of the bladder, and can be horribly painful however it's achieved. The most common cause is an infection of *E.coli* bacteria, and symptoms include burning when you wee, needing to wee all the time, even when you've just been, and, occasionally, cloudy wee. It's annoyingly common, and women suffer much more often than men – because we have shorter urethras so any foreign bacteria have a much higher chance of ascending to the bladder unhampered. Also, any kind of roughness during sex can rub and bruise it, so it ends up inflamed. It's much more likely to get you if you tend to get dehydrated during the day, because the bacteria can multiply without being flushed out – so it's back to the tedious old supermodel trick of drinking two litres of water a day. But just think – you won't have cystitis – and what's more, you'll be modelling the spring collections in no time. Treatment, once again, is a combination of antibiotics and lots of water. Also, cranberry juice is excellent for bladder health – so a fine excuse to whisk up a tray of Sea Breezes, then. Maybe.

excuses for catching an STD

When you visit the clinic, memorize this list. To minimize embarrassment, only use excuses from list two.

POOR EXCUSES

1. 'I didn't want to look as if I was making a fuss, so I didn't ask him to use a condom.'
2. 'It must have been off the toilet seat. All three men I slept with last week looked clean, I swear.'
3. 'I thought those boils on his penis were just lumpy veins.'

GOOD EXCUSES

1. 'He slept with someone else and passed it onto me.'
2. 'I must have caught it two years ago, but the symptoms have only just appeared.'
3. 'The condom broke.'

CHAPTER SIXTEEN

Top tips for a great sex life

If I were asked for a one line answer to the question 'What makes a woman good in bed?' I would say, 'A man who is good in bed.'

Bob Guccione (*Penthouse* founder)

So, by now you should be able to navigate your way fairly expertly around any bed containing a willing man. You're clued up on positions, seduction, kissing, oral, manual ... In fact, you're a sex goddess. But, while by now you should possess enough knowledge (if not experience) to render him a quivering wreck with desire, you can never have enough sex tips up your sleeve. Or down your knickers, for that matter. So, to finish off, we'll take a look at the top 20 of sex tips that will ensure your sexual experiences will never again involve thinking, 'I really must paint that ceiling', and more 'I really must swing from that chandelier.' But only if it's firmly screwed in, obviously. I'd hate you to get hurt, after all I've taught you ...

1. Gichigich

You sit on his lap, and he puts his penis between your legs. Here, you have to persuade him that sticking it in isn't really the point. Because what he has to do is just gently rub himself up and down between your labia and over your clitoris. He can use his hand, your hand, or just his muscles to move his penis around. Needless to say, it'll feel fantastic to him – but it'll feel even better to you. It avoids the usual intercourse problem of not enough stimulation, but it provides the thrill of genital contact, and is gentler than fingers. And it's called gichigich, by its inventors, a tribe from Oceania. So perhaps it's best to show him what you mean, rather than ask for it by name. Just in case he misinterprets your request as you choking on a peanut.

2. The sex inventory

The number of open-minded, sexually confident women who still lie there thinking, 'If only he'd do that ...' but don't know how to ask is mind-boggling. Which is why the Sex Inventory is such a good idea. It sounds like a court document, but in practice it could revolutionize your sex life. All it involves is writing down what you both want – but you have to be absolutely specific. Divide it into 'Setting the Mood', 'Arousal', 'Orgasm' and 'Afterplay', and in each section write as much as you want – 'I want you to kiss my face all over with little feathery kisses,' rather than 'More affection'. Most bed problems are down to lack of communication – he might be under the impression that you love having your buttocks squeezed when actually it makes you feel like a loaf being kneaded. Write down what you really want instead, and get him to do the same (but don't say anything negative about his past technique). Then compare lists, and take turns to put your requests into practice.

3. Penetrative orgasm? Yeah, right

Orgasm at the moment of penetration? Hah! A ridiculous myth put about by male pornographers, no? Well, no. If you're very,

very aroused, it is possible to come the minute he pops it in. The key to this is to keep bringing yourself to the edge of orgasm, by rubbing his penis against your clitoris, for about 15 minutes – but don't insert it. Alternate this with giving him oral sex, to keep him in a constant state of huge arousal. Remain as relaxed as is humanly possible, and don't concentrate on having an orgasm – just concentrate on what you're doing. Then, as you teeter on the brink of a crashing orgasm, take a deep breath and thrust yourself right onto his penis, sliding all the way down. If it doesn't happen, at least trying might be fun.

4. Turning circle

Of course, in the Ancient East, acrobatic positions were nothing special because they had the *Kama Sutra* to while away the dark evenings (possibly the best sex book ever written – or at least the most comprehensive). One of the best positions in it is The Turning Position. Now listen carefully. Begin in the missionary position, his legs between yours. Without pulling out of you, he lifts first left leg then right leg over your right leg. (Still with me? Good.) Keep your legs slightly apart, to make it easier for him stay inside you. Now, supporting himself on his arms, he moves both legs round, until his body's lying sideways across you. And then, finally, he repeats the second stage, so he's lying with his body between your legs and one leg each side of your shoulders. And the whole procedure should give rise to some very unusual sensations for both of you. It'll certainly tire you out, at any rate. If this seems a bit risky, you can do it with him underneath. But be careful not to bend his willy back, won't you?

5. Dancing in the dark

Doing it at night, in the dark, may seem to describe the sexual world of your grandparents. However, sometimes we're so hung up about our bodies, and focused on what's going on around us, that we can't let go and enjoy sex, and simply focus on each other. So if you switch the light out and go by touch alone, you won't think, 'Oh my God, the size of my arse ...' and he won't be thinking 'Now she's looking at my beer gut, now she's thinking I'm Homer Simpson.' Instead, you'll be able to focus purely on the sensations you're experiencing. According to this theory, it's best to make love at night, because at the end of the day you feel you've earned the right to relax, and are likely to be more focused to the idea of sex. Which is, in my view, good advice – there's nothing wrong with a daytime delight, but it loses its magic when you're worrying about getting back to work afterwards. And, as for early-morning sex ... come on, really? Does anyone do that? No!

6. Aphrodisiacs

The whole idea of aphrodisiacs is vaguely questionable – because there's no scientific proof they work. However, some foods are worth trying simply because they are deeply sensual to eat. And I'm not talking about the *Lady and the Tramp* spaghetti scene. I'm talking about exotic fruit, mousses (not mooses, unless you're a Canadian bear-trapper), asparagus, and anything else that's simple and attractive to eat. Certain foods resemble the genitals (oysters, courgettes, marrows, if you're lucky ...) and are therefore a turn-on to eat in front of a partner. And some are stuffed with chemicals that promote lustful feelings – fish is full of zinc, which enhances sperm production, and chocolate is full of phenylethamine, the 'falling in love' chemical. Even lettuce can be aphrodisiac – it's a diuretic, which means it makes the urinary tract itchy, and therefore stimulates your genitals. Weird. Non-food aphrodisiacs are useless, apart from champagne, which is the best drug ever invented to get you in the mood. But be warned – if you think beer goggles are dangerous, wearing champagne goggles out on the pull could mean you end up with Mick Hucknall's uglier brother, having been convinced you were making sweet music with Ralph Fiennes all night. As for Spanish fly, and its ilk – forget it. It's illegal, expensive, and it'll probably kill you. Apart from that, it's great ...

7. High heels

A simple yet highly effective sex tip. You may well be the kind of girl who can't imagine doing anything in high heels, who boasts about her 15 kinds of trainers, and thinks marabou is a coconut liqueur drunk by Japanese people ... but it's time you burst out of your 'little miss sensible' straitjacket, and embraced the goddess of the boudoir. You don't have to walk anywhere in them – they aren't for work. They're to make your legs look unbelievably sexy in stockings, and make your partner dizzy with desire. He may well desire you without the stilettos – but with, you'll be irresistible, as you embody every filthy fantasy he's ever had regarding mysterious call-girls, beautiful Bond girls, and frustrated housewives. Choose ones with ankle straps as a) they're excessively provocative, and b) they're less likely to fly off and give him a black eye.

8. Oil slide

Another trick borrowed from the bar girls and possibly, lady-boys of Bangkok. The oil slide is simplicity itself, but feels fantastic. All you do – using old sheets, ideally – is get him to lie back naked on the bed, and take all your clothes off. Cover your entire body – paying special attention to the front – in oil. Then, starting at his feet, press your shoulders against him. Pull yourself up slowly , using your arms, and wiggling from side to side, till you're sliding gently over his entire body, full-frontally. Feel free to gyrate around, and slide back and forth, but keep the moves slow – nothing jerky, mind. And when you get to the top, just add more oil and go back down again. Just don't use a condom afterwards, as it'll rot – somewhat less than erotic, but worth bearing in mind, eh?

9. Ice cubes

I know, you've heard it all before ... ice-cube blowjobs indeed – who can be bothered? Well you can, actually, madam, because it may be the best-beloved tip of a thousand magazines, but that's because, for once, it actually works. All you do, just before giving him a blowjob, is pop an ice cube in your mouth. One that's been in a glass of something delicious and alcoholic, rather than one straight from the freezer that's going to stick agonizingly to your tongue, and his penis, however – fasten your mouth over his willy, with the cube balanced at the tip, and swirl it around on him. The immediate cold will quickly be replaced with heat, as your tongue warms up the icy bits. If you wish, you can alternate between cube and mouthfuls of hot tea (or Irish coffee, if you want to keep the 'alcohol' theme going) and he will be quickly lost in a world of giddy sensation. Of course, he can do the same for you – as long as he keeps that cube moving. You don't want to feel like you've had a local anaesthetic on your clitoris.

10. Mirrors

For the aspiring voyeur, you can't beat sex in front of a mirror. It also works for the narcissist too, who loves looking at him or herself. And even the casual exhibitionist. In fact, it's a winner all round, if you can ignore your flabby bits, and concentrate only on watching the sensual drama unfold, as you make passionate love before an audience of ... yourselves. If your fantasy is to be watched, or you've always wanted to see what your partner looks like taking you from behind, a large mirror is the answer. Watching yourselves is a major turn-on, without the terror of video ('Ohmigod, one day we might have kids and they might find the tape, your mother might come to stay and think it's *The Horse Whisperer*, oh Christ ...'). But I suggest you use an old mirror, which has a soft glow to it, coupled with candlelight, to give your skin an apricot sheen, and make you look as if you're starring in a high-production-values BBC adaptation, rather than having a quickie in the loos of a service station.

11. Bums

So far, the buttocks have been cruelly ignored – which is odd, considering that they're a major sexual signal, and their shape is an erotic trigger for both sexes. They are, in fact, worth paying a lot of attention to in bed – they're a major surface area, packed with nerves, and stroking them can be incredibly sexy – alternate between light fingertip-stroking, and kneading as if you're making bread (well, gentle bread – not some rough, wholegrain thing), and pay particular attention to the cleft at the top. Of course, if you so desire you can explore further down the crack – but, if not, there's a lot to be said for simple caressing, which fires up nerves all over the body. Using massage oil can drive the bum-kneading recipient to heights of passion – so you may find your fingers stray round the front after a relatively short time.

12. Hold your tum in

In the midst of orgasm, you're unlikely to bother thinking about complicated ways to intensify it. So here's a very simple way. All you need to do, as you approach the moment of explosion, is pull your stomach muscles in, as if you're trying to squeeze into a dress that's a size smaller than normal. This has the magical effect of making you breathe more shallowly, thus building up tension, and making your orgasm more intense. Though that doesn't mean that if you go around sucking your stomach in you'll be on a constant sexual high – you'll probably just go blue and faint.

13. Semi-thrust

Without wishing to go all tantric on you, there is a technique, as promoted by inner-oneness types, which does actually work very well when it comes to making sex amazing. All he has to do is alternate between slow and fast thrusting, which sounds simple enough. But, in fact, it takes major control for him not to think, 'Wahey, race to the finish', and leap about like a spawning salmon the moment your genitals meet. So if he does wish to emulate the tantric masters, get him to vary between six shallow thrusts and six deep thrusts – well, you may not be able to count exactly – and switch between slow and fast. Not knowing what kind of stroke you'll get next is highly arousing – and when he thrusts hard after a series of gentle in-and-outs, you'll be picking yourselves off the ceiling. Which probably isn't very good feng shui, but never mind, it's worth it.

14. Shower soap

I've already explained exactly why sex in the bath isn't worth the effort. Sex in the shower, too, can be a recipe for a broken leg and dismal recriminations. But foreplay in the shower is an entirely different ballgame. It's that soap-and-water thing, you see – no skin friction, it's all smooth, and you can wash each other all over without snagging your hands on annoying hairs, or bits of dry skin. Obviously, it won't be long till he's touching your breasts, and you're rubbing his willy, aided by shower gel – it'll help if there's a rail somewhere to hold onto, as you don't want to slip in the heat of passion. And try not to use scented soap, if it gets into your bits: it can sting like mad. One more warning – don't be tempted to wash each other's hair, as you'll get soap in your eyes, and feel like a three-year-old waiting to be rinsed. Not at all sexy.

15. Phone sex

Most people find talking dirty rather awkward at first. Murmuring 'Ride me like a tiger' is all very well in certain films, but when you know you're meeting over breakfast next day to talk about weekend food shopping, it's all rather un-British and embarrassing. Which is where phone sex comes in handy. Because you can't see each other's faces, it's much easier to let loose and express your innermost perverted fantasies without worrying about whether his face is contorted with passion, or simply repressed smirking. It helps if he's not at the office – a business trip is the perfect excuse for late-night phoning from bed. Simply start by telling him you aren't wearing much, then progress to describing exactly what he'd be doing to you, if he was there. You can aid the process with a glass of wine or three, if you feel shy – besides, he'll give you more than enough encouragement. The idea is that you both masturbate naked – but if you're really tired, you can wear fluffy pyjamas and just pant a bit to give him the idea. Unless you have a videophone.

16. Polaroids

Taking sexy photos can enhance your erotic life no end – it can also make you a laughing stock when the bloke from the dodgy developer's lab recognizes you in the pub. Which is, obviously, why the Polaroid camera is such a useful invention. You get 12 pictures, all of which develop instantly – and so you can pose in whatever outfits and positions you wish, with no danger of anyone thinking, 'Hang on, isn't that ...?' as you walk down the street. You can destroy them afterwards, or present them to your partner to examine at leisure when you're not around. But if you are going to do that, make absolutely sure that he hasn't got a scanner and a grudge-bearing mentality. One day, you may dump him – and you really don't want you dressed as a French maid emailed to your bosses, do you? Unless you work for a strippergram company, of course, and it's time for promotion.

17. Ears and necks

For some reason, your ears and neck are absolutely packed with nerve-endings. Maybe this is a Stone Age throwback, so you don't get flies in your ears, because your nerves tingle as soon as one flies near. I just don't know. But the upside of this is, they are almost certainly your greatest erogenous zones after genitals and breasts. All he has to do is pay them some attention – and I don't mean squishing his tongue round them as if they're in need of a good clean. Think of the whole area as a giant clitoris, which responds best to gentle, feathery touches from his lips and tongue. He should run the tip lightly round your ear, rather than thrusting it inside, and trail his lips gently along your neck just below your earlobe. He can also suck your lobes, as long as you aren't wearing earrings – otherwise, he may end up with a diamanté stud lodged in his windpipe. Blowing into your ear – gently, mind – can be a major turn-on, and all-over neck kissing should, with luck, reduce you to the sort of tingling wreck who'll agree to anything. Actually, on second thoughts, is that such a good thing?

18. Shaving

Just try and rid your mind of the porn mag delightfully titled *Shaven Haven*. I know the whole concept of shaving your pubes off is slightly less appealing than waxing your chin. But if you've a mind to experiment, the whole thing can be a thoroughly worthwhile experience (apart from when they grow back – then it's just itchy). I'd recommend that you perform the shave yourself – otherwise, it'll be less erotic, more petrifying. Snip off the long bits, then go round the stubble with a razor (electric may be safer – hey, and offer a thrill). You can whip the lot off, or leave a 'landing strip' of an inch or so. The benefit of all this hassle is it looks sexy, as he can see everything, laid bare, as it were – and it's much easier to generate friction during sex, because your natural 'cushion' has gone. Which means your clitoris gets more excitement. Just a word – don't attempt shaving when you're drunk, will you? I once shaved a guy's face (and that was just his face, remember) after a bottle of wine, and I've never seen such white-knuckled fear. I don't know what he was thinking of to let me, quite honestly …

19. Strip Twister

A simple yet effective variant on the old 'strip poker' thing. With strip Twister, however, it's just a matter of time before the game ensures you're having sex. You don't actually have to do much at all, and you certainly don't have to remember any complex rules. Just position yourself at the edges of the mat, spin the arrow, and do what it says – 'right hand green' or 'left foot blue'. As soon as one of you falls over, you take something off. Once naked, carry on playing and, once you fall over, have sex. He'll be lying on top of you anyway, so you may as well. If you're feeling exhibitionist, simply get him to whirl the spinner, while you gyrate through a series of pornographic positions. Either way, let's face it – you're going to end up having sex. And, unlike poker, you aren't going to feel a failure for losing.

20. And finally ...

This is the cheesy, final, mind-how-you-go bit, where the DJ comes on and says, 'You've been a great audience, God bless.' So, in keeping with that, here is the final and most important sex tip, which you should always recall as you live your sex goddess life ... and it's simply this: never do anything that destroys your self-respect. You can do anything you like, as long as you feel good about it. But if you're not happy, or you've been persuaded into it, against your better judgment, or you're only doing it because you feel you should ... just don't. Apart from that ... well, you have a good time. And if you don't know how to do that by now, you really can't blame me – I've taught you everything I know.